Management Handbook
for
Pharmacy Practitioners

A Practical Guide for Community Pharmacists

Management Handbook
for
Pharmacy Practitioners

A Practical Guide for Community Pharmacists

Health Sciences Consortium, Inc.

ISBN 0-938938-08-8
Library of Congress Catalog Number: 82-48578
© Copyright, 1982, by the Upjohn Company
All rights reserved. No part of this publication
may be reproduced by any means without the permission
of the publisher.
Address requests to the Health Sciences Consortium, Inc.
200 Eastowne Drive, Suite 213; Chapel Hill, North Carolina 27514

Management Handbook for Pharmacy Practitioners:
A Practical Guide for Community Pharmacists
was set in ten point Press Roman
at Bull City Studios,
Durham, North Carolina

Cover: Josephine A. Killeffer & Bogara

Printed in United States of America

TABLE OF CONTENTS

This publication was made possible through a grant from the Upjohn Company.

PREFACE

In the fall of 1980, the Health Sciences Consortium, through a grant from The Upjohn Company, conducted a workshop on instructional materials development for instructors of pharmacy administration in Chapel Hill, North Carolina. The goals of this workshop were to identify and then produce instructional units on management strategies that were comprehensive, effective, and easily implemented or applied, in a community pharmacy setting. By the end of the two-day workshop, most of the preliminary work toward achieving these goals had been completed.

Over the next year, the Consortium staff worked closely with the various authors in the completion of their instrucional units. Most of the material used in the preparation of the manuscripts had originated from lecture notes prepared by faculty for use in undergraduate pharmacy administration courses. In most cases, these individuals had taken basic business techniques and, through consultation with practitioners, had adapted their lecture notes for use in community pharmacy operations. Their teaching experience, their managerial skills, and their understanding of the relationship of sound management to pharmacy practice were all combined in this endeavor. After extensive peer review of the manuscripts and exhaustive instructional design review and editing by the staff of the Health Sciences Consortium, eight clear, concise self-instructional units were produced.

The purpose of this book is not to present a complete collection of all managerial strategies; instead, it is a compendium of information that presents a selected number of basic managerial tools that, when implemented, should increase a pharmacy owner/manager's control of a pharmacy. The advice and guidance offered in this book address the primary areas that account for the majority of problems encountered in the daily operation of the community pharmacy. If practitioners find this book informative and conducive to good management practice, the goals of this project will have been achieved.

INTRODUCTION

Community pharmacy management has become an increasingly important topic among practitioners over the last few years. Pharmacy managers have become increasingly attentive to innovative managerial techniques as a result of declining profits and decreased return-on-investment caused by intense competitive pressures coupled with inflationary rises in operating costs. Moreover, because of consumer price sensitivity and the complexity of modern pharmacy management, pharmacy owner/managers are aware, now more than ever, that on-the-job management training is not enough to manage a pharmacy satisfactorily. They need practical and relevant suggestions and guidance for directing and monitoring the activities within their businesses.

Fortunately, there exists a body of management literature that contains information that could be readily adopted and implemented for use in the community pharmacy. The problems confronting community pharmacy practitioners, however, are a) locating the information, b) understanding the theory, and c) applying current methodology to their own particular setting. This book assists community pharmacists in solving serious management problems. It contains eight instructional units which offer guidelines for overcoming difficulties in the following areas: inventory, accounts receivable, cash flow, merchandising, basic recordkeeping, taxes, and advertising. In addition, the use of an important managerial tool, the break-even analysis, is also discussed.

N.B.: In this program, where no antecedent has been established, only masculine pronouns are used, for simplicity, in referring to both males and females. In such cases, these forms should be viewed as common and not gender-specific.

Unit One

Basic Business Records
for a Community Pharmacy

Edward J. Zabloski, M.B.A., C.M.A.
Assistant Treasurer
Philip Cooper Associates, Inc.

Colman M. Herman, Ph.D.
Associate Professor
Massachusettes College of
Pharmacy and Allied Health Sciences

TABLE OF CONTENTS

Study Time: **1.5 hours**
CE Credit: **.15 CEU**

INTRODUCTION

Basic business records for a community pharmacy is essentially the discipline of pharmacy accounting. This discipline includes the design of a system of records, subsequent recording of accounting data, and the periodic summation of the data. This periodic summation of data occurs for such external reporting purposes as reports to taxing authorities and prospective creditors as well as for internal managerial purposes. Additional recordkeeping considerations with respect to payroll accounting are essential aspects of this discipline.

The purpose of this program is to aid the pharmacy owner/manager in identifying the basic business records to be maintained for a community pharmacy. Not all pharmacies have the same recordkeeping needs, therefore, information is provided in this program to aid the pharmacy owner/manager in the design of an appropriate system of records. This involves the selection of the correct accounting base and appropriate journals and ledgers. The summarizing of information in the form of financial statements and payroll accounting is examined. Lastly, the sources of professional accounting help are identified to aid the owner/manager in designing or maintaining the system of records as well as in summarizing accumulated data.

OBJECTIVES

The objectives are presented here to aid the user in focusing attention on expected learning outcomes.

Upon completion of this unit, the user should be able to:

1. Differentiate between users of the cash and accrual bases of accounting.

2. Define the recording of information process as it relates to the use of a) the chart of accounts, b) the journalizing process, c) the posting process, and d) the adjusting process.

3. Recognize ways of alleviating accounting problems created by sales and purchases merchandising cycles.

4. Identify appropriate functions of the following special journals and subsidiary ledgers when used in concert with the general journal and general ledger:

   a. sales journal
   b. purchase journal
   c. cash receipts journal
   d. cash payments journal
   e. subsidiary accounts receivable ledger
   f. subsidiary accounts payable ledger

5. Identify the interrelationship of the following financial statements:

   a. income statement
   b. statement of owner's equity
   c. balance sheet

6. Calculate items found in financial statements given appropriate data.

7. Characterize the following payroll related items:
   a. payroll employees
   b. withholding from an employee's pay
   c. payroll taxes

8. Identify individuals who may provide assistance in the design of the system of records for a community pharmacy.

RECOMMENDED PREPARATION

Prior to the use of this unit, the user should be familiar with common pharmaceutical accounting terminology. This may be accomplished by studying the definitions of common accounting terms listed below. Additional background information may be obtained from the following reference.

Marino, F., Zabloski, E., and Herman, C. *Principles of Pharmaceutical Accounting.* Philadelphia, PA: Lea & Febiger, 1980. Chapters 1-6.

GLOSSARY OF TERMS

Assets: the economic resources owned by a firm that will yield some future benefit. They are subdivided into current assets, fixed assets, and other assets.

Current assets: resources that can be converted into cash or are consumed in the operation of a business within one year. Current assets are responsible for providing a flow of cash to sustain a firm's day-to-day operations. They normally constitute about 75% of the total assets of a pharmacy. Typical examples include cash, accounts receivable, inventory, and supplies.

Fixed assets: tangible, productive resources used in the operation of a firm are called fixed assets. They have a useful life of more than one year and cannot be sold without seriously disrupting the operation of a business. Common examples of fixed assets encountered in a pharmacy include furniture and fixtures, a delivery vehicle, building, and land.

Other assets: a miscellaneous category of assets not usually found in a pharmacy. Examples are leaseholds, leasehold improvements, franchises, and goodwill.

Liabilities: represent the claims of creditors against the assets of a firm. They may be subdivided into current liabilities and long-term liabilities.

Current liabilities: include all debts that must be paid within one year. Examples found in a typical pharmacy are accounts payable, notes payable, salaries payable, taxes payable, and utilities payable.

Long-term liabilities: include all debts that are not due within one year. Notes payable and loans payable may be long-term liabilities if the terms specify that repayment is not due for at least one year. Mortgage payable is another example of a long-term liability often found in a pharmacy.

Owner's equity: also called net worth (or simply, capital) represents the claim of the owner against the assets of a firm, based on the amount of money personally invested. It is residual or secondary to the claims of the creditors because, in the event that the business is liquidated and the assets are sold, the creditors must be paid before the owner can receive any money.

Revenues: inflow of cash or other assets arising from the provision of goods or services to patrons of a firm. Revenues from a pharmacy are derived from prescription drug sales, nonprescription drug sales, nursing home consultant fees, and health and beauty aid sales.

Expenses: involve the consumption of goods or services in the operation of a firm. They are generally incurred in order to generate revenue. Common examples in the pharmacy are salaries and wages, rent, utilities, advertising, and insurance.

Net income: when total revenues exceed total expenses, the result is called net income or net profit. Conversely, when total expenses exceed total revenues, the result is referred to as net loss.

Financial statements: the term referring collectively to the balance sheet, the income statement, and the statement of owner's equity.

I. ACCOUNTING BASES

A pharmacy owner/manager may choose between two methods of accounting, cash basis and accrual basis, although for the reasons stated below, accrual basis is recommended. The cash basis of accounting states that: 1) revenue is recognized and recorded at the point in time when cash is received, regardless of when it is earned; and 2) an expense is recognized and recorded at the point in time when payment is made for goods or services, regardless of when they are consumed. On the other hand, the accrual basis of accounting states that: 1) revenue is recognized and recorded at the point in time when goods or services are consumed, regardless of when payment is made; and 2) an expense is recognized and recorded at the point in time when it is incurred, regardless of when payment is made.

As an example, assume that on April 10 a pharmacist dispenses prescription medication to a charge patient who pays the total bill on April 25. Under the cash basis of accounting, the revenue would be recognized on April 25, whereas, with the accrual method, the revenue would be recognized on April 10. As another example, assume that on August 8 a pharmacist pays a $75 bill for prescription containers that will be used in August, September, and October. With the cash basis of accounting, the $75 expense is recognized on August 8, whereas, with the accrual method, the expense is recognized as the vials are consumed.

Principal users of the cash basis of accounting are people such as physicians, attorneys, accountants, consultants, and hairdressers. The primary benefit lies in its simplicity. Its use by a pharmacy, however, would result in the distortion of financial data because merchandise inventories would not be accounted for as an asset when purchased, but rather as an expense. Given the importance and size of inventory in a typical pharmacy, the accrual basis of accounting is, therefore, recommended for adoption. In addition to providing a more accurate presentation of financial data, a pharmacy owner/manager using the accrual basis of accounting would be in a better position to compare data with the data of other pharmacies presented in the *Lilly Digest,* a publication that presents industry averages.

II. INFORMATION RECORDING SYSTEMS

The financial activities of a pharmacy consist of a series of economic events called transactions that serve as the building blocks of the accounting and financial system. Transactions involve an exchange of value, measured in dollars, between two or more individuals or organizations. The most common exchange consists of the receipt of cash for goods or services. Some transactions, such as paying a telephone or electric bill, are simple, independent events. Others are more complicated; for example, the dispensing of a drug to a patient with a charge account is an exchange of value, i.e., the drug for a promise to pay. It suggests, however, that another transaction will occur at a later date, i.e., the collection of cash from the patient.

Many pharmacies dispense from 50 to 100 or more prescriptions per day. To this must be added many other transactions such as nonprescription drug sales, health and beauty aid sales, and nursing home consultant fees, to name a few. Moreover, as a pharmacy expands, its transactions become more varied, affecting a larger number of assets, liabilities, revenues, and expenses. When these factors are considered, it can be concluded that a streamlined accounting system is required to accommodate all transactions encountered in a typical pharmacy. Such a system begins with the chart of accounts and involves the use of a general journal and a general ledger.

The main component of the journal and ledger system is a separate record called an account—one for each asset, liability, owner's equity, revenue, and expense. The account serves as a central place where transaction data are accumulated. Each transaction will affect at least two accounts, giving rise to the concept of double-entry accounting. One account exists for each item appearing on the financial statements, with a small pharmacy requiring as few as 30 accounts and a larger pharmacy needing three to four times as many.

A. CHART OF ACCOUNTS

A chart of accounts, presented in Table 1, should be prepared to list all the accounts used by a firm in the order of their appearance on the financial statement, i.e., assets, followed in order by liabilities, owner's equity, revenues, and expenses. The accounts should be numbered sequentially, with room left for the introduction of new accounts. The numbering system should allow for the rapid identification of the types of accounts. For example, all assets could be numbered from 101 to 199 and all liabilities could be numbered from 201 to 299. In addition to serving as an index to the accounts, the chart assists in assuring the use of authorized accounts only, and the correct accounts may be used to record transaction data.

B. GENERAL JOURNAL

The general journal is a chronological listing of the transactions of the pharmacy, with each entry serving to record the complete data from one transaction. Each journal entry refers to the particular accounts involved in the transaction. Table 2 presents the typical format of a page in a general journal, with a sample entry involving the payment of the February rent on January 25th.

TABLE 1. Example of a Chart of Accounts
(Adapted from the *Lilly Digest*)

Account Number	Account Title
101	Assets: Cash
111	Accounts receivable
113	Inventory
140	Land
150	Building
160	Fixtures
170	Equipment
180	Leasehold improvements
190	Prepaid expenses
201	Liabilities: Accounts payable
202	Notes payable
211	Accrued expenses
250	Long-term notes payable
301	Capital: Owner, capital
310	Owner, drawing
401	Revenue: Sales
501	Expenses: Cost of goods sold
510	Employees' wages & salaries
515	Rent
520	Heat, light & power
525	Accounting, legal and other professional fees
530	Taxes
535	Insurance
540	Interest
545	Repairs
550	Delivery
555	Advertising
560	Depreciation
565	Bad debts
570	Telephone
575	Miscellaneous

A debit refers to the left money column of an account or to the amount entered in the column. A credit refers to the right money column of an account or to the amount entered in the column. Since debits and credits are not inherently equal to increases or decreases, it is necessary to know the rules of debit and credit. An increase in an asset account, owner withdrawal account, or expense account is recorded by a debit, whereas, a decrease is indicated by a credit. Conversely, an increase in a liability account, owner capital account, or revenue account is recorded by a credit, whereas, a decrease is indicated by a debit. The total debits must equal the total credits in all journal entries.

TABLE 2. General Journal Format

				Page 20	
Date	Account Title and Explanation	F*	Debit	Credit	
Jan 25	Rent Expense	515	300—		1
	Cash	101		300—	2
					3
					4
					5

*The F (folio) column is used to record the account number, after posting to the general ledger is completed.

C. GENERAL LEDGER

A general ledger consists of a compilation of the transaction data by account. Through a process called *posting,* the data is transferred from the general journal to the general ledger. The ledger may take the form of a loose-leaf book with one or more pages allocated to each account, a tray of unit-record (punch) cards, or a computer printout derived from data stored on magnetic tapes or disks.

One common format for a ledger is the *T-account,* presented in Table 3. It is so called because it is divided by a "T" into debit and credit sides corresponding to those found in the general journal. The posting of the debit entry (rent expense) to the general ledger from the general journal shown in Table 2 is included in Table 3.

TABLE 3. General T-Account Format

		Account Title: Rent Expense	F*	Debit	Date	Account #: 515	F*	Credit	
1									1
2	Jan 25	February	20	300—					2
3									3
4									4
5									5

*The F (folio) column is used to record the page number of the journal represented by the transaction.

A chart of accounts, general journal, and general ledger represent the minimum basic records for an information recording system for a community pharmacy. However, pharmacies are merchandising firms, and may be involved in either or both of the merchandising cycles depicted in Figure 1.

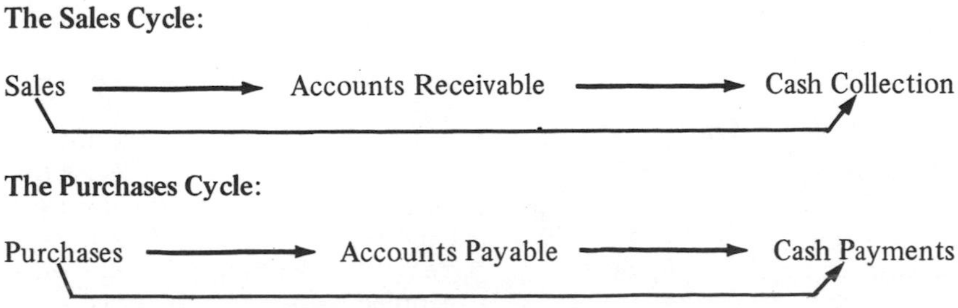

The Sales Cycle:

Sales ⟶ Accounts Receivable ⟶ Cash Collection

The Purchases Cycle:

Purchases ⟶ Accounts Payable ⟶ Cash Payments

FIGURE 1. Merchandising Cycles

The normal recording of transactions in the general journal and subsequent posting to the general ledger does not provide information as to how much a pharmacy owes to each individual supplier and how much each individual patron owes to the pharmacy. One way for a pharmacy to avoid problems created by merchandising cycles would be to eliminate a charge system for patrons and to acquire all purchases from one supplier, such as a wholesaler. Of course, it may not be economically feasible for a pharmacy to have a cash-only business or one-supply source.

As an alternative solution to this problem, a separate accounts payable account could be established for each supplier, and a separate accounts receivable account could be established for each patron. However, if the pharmacy has a large number of suppliers and credit patrons, the general ledger would become too cumbersome to be efficient.

D. SUBSIDIARY LEDGERS

The best solution to problems created by merchandising cycles involves the use of two subsidiary ledgers, one for accounts payable and one for accounts receivable. The accounts payable subsidiary ledger would contain individual accounts for each supplier, while the accounts receivable subsidiary ledger would contain individual accounts for each credit patron. General ledger entries for accounts payable and receivable still would occur, with the accounts being referred to as control accounts, i.e., *accounts payable control* and *accounts receivable control*.

In addition to a subsidiary accounts receivable ledger and a subsidiary accounts payable ledger, the accounting system can be modified to deal efficiently with the growing number of transactions of a pharmacy. The modification involves the use of four special journals, one each for cash receipts, cash payments, credit sales, and credit purchases. These special journals are intended to supplement, but not replace entirely, the general journal. The cash receipts journal is used to record all transactions that involve the immediate *receipt* of cash. The cash payments journal is used to record all transactions that involve the immediate *payment* of cash. The credit sales journal is used to record all transactions that involve the sale of merchandise to a patron on account. The credit purchases journal is used to record all transactions that involve the purchase of merchandise from a supplier on account. Postings from special journals are made daily to the subsidiary ledgers and usually monthly to the general journal.

REVIEW QUESTIONS (I & II)

DIRECTIONS: Circle the letter corresponding to the correct answer for each of the following.

1. The filling of a prescription on account for a patron would be recorded as a transaction of the pharmacy at the time

   a. the prescription is dispensed under the cash basis of accounting.

   b. cash is received under both the cash basis and accrual basis of accounting.

   c. the prescription is dispensed under the accrual basis of accounting.

   d. both b and c.

   e. both a and b.

2. The minimum basic records for an information recording system for a community pharmacy are

   a. the sales cycle and the purchases cycle.
   b. the chart of accounts, the general journal, and the general ledger.
   c. special journals and subsidiary ledgers.
   d. both b and c.
   e. both a and b.

3. A pharmacy that acquires all purchases from one wholesaler avoids the accounting problems created by

   a. the sales cycle.
   b. the purchases cycle.
   c. both the sales and the purchases cycles.
   d. neither the sales nor the purchases cycles.

Check your responses on page 22.

III. SUMMATION OF DATA

Recorded data for certain time periods must be transformed into summarized data in the form of financial statements. In keeping with the practices of the accrual basis of accounting, such transformations take the form of adjustments for the purpose of updating accounts so that the financial statements are more accurate.

A. FINANCIAL STATEMENTS

The transactions that enter the accounting system ultimately will be used to generate three financial statements: the balance sheet (statement of financial position), income statement, and statement of owner's equity.

1. *Balance Sheet.* Table 4 presents an example of a balance sheet for a pharmacy. The top of the balance sheet consists of the name of the firm, the words "Balance Sheet" and the specific point in time represented by the statement. Its purpose is to summarize the assets, liabilities, and owner's equity of a business.

2. *Income Statement.* Table 5 presents an example of an income statement for a pharmacy. Like the balance sheet, the top of the income statement contains the name of the firm and words identifying the particular statement. Unlike the balance sheet, the income statement is prepared for a period of time, e.g., for the year ended June 30, 19X7, rather than for a specific point in time, e.g., June 30, 19X7. Thus, the balance sheet is time-static, while the income statement is time-dynamic. The purpose of the income statement is to summarize the revenues, expenses, and net income (net profit) or net loss of a business.

3. *Statement of Owner's Equity.* Table 6 presents an example of a statement of owner's equity. Like the balance sheet and the income statement, the top of this statement includes the name of the firm and the words identifying the statement. Unlike the balance sheet, but like the income statement, the statement of owner's equity is issued for a period of time, e.g., for the year ended June 30, 19X7. It is, therefore, a time-dynamic rather than a time-static statement.

The statement of owner's equity consists of beginning capital, owner investments, net income or net loss, owner withdrawals, and ending capital. Investment of cash or property in a firm, by the owner, and net income increase owner's equity, whereas loss and withdrawals of cash or property from the business, by the owner, decrease owner's equity. Withdrawals are not business expenses because they do not generate revenue.

TABLE 4. An Example of a Balance Sheet
(Adapted from the *Lilly Digest*)

X Pharmacy
Balance Sheet
June 30, 19X7

Assets
Current Assets
  Cash . . . . $ 12,296.00
  Accounts receivable 13,462.00
  Inventory 58,276.00
  Total current assets . . . . $ 84,034.00
Fixed Assets
  Fixtures and equipment and leasehold
    improvements (net after reserve for
    depreciation) 13,771.00
Other Assets
  Prepaid expenses, deposits, etc. 5,357.00
  Total assets $103,162.00

Liabilities
Current and Accrued Liabilities
  Accounts payable . . . . $ 16,633.00
  Notes payable (within one year) 5,620.00
  Accrued expenses and other liabilities 5,503.00
  Total current and accrued liabilities . . . . $ 27,756.00
Long-Term Liabilities
  Notes payable (due more than
    one year later) 16,407.00
  Total liabilities . . . . $ 44,163.00

Net Worth 58,999.00
Total Liabilities and Net Worth $103,162.00

TABLE 5. An Example of an Income Statement
(Adapted from the *Lilly Digest*)

X Pharmacy
Income Statement
Year Ended June 30, 19X7

Total Sales	$345,302.00
Cost of Goods Sold	225,651.00
Gross Margin	$119,651.00

Expenses

Employees' wages	39,914.00
Rent	8,436.00
Heat, light, and power	3,024.00
Accounting, legal and other professional fees	1,518.00
Taxes (except on buildings, income, and profit) and licenses	5,132.00
Insurance (except on buildings)	3,747.00
Interest paid	2,160.00
Repairs	1,091.00
Delivery	1,502.00
Advertising	4,004.00
Depreciation (except on buildings)	3,028.00
Bad debts charged off	482.00
Telephone	1,280.00
Miscellaneous	8,970.00
Total Expenses	$ 84,288.00
Net Profit (before taxes & owner withdrawals)	$ 35,363.00

TABLE 6. An Example of a Statement of Owner's Equity
(Adapted from the *Lilly Digest*)

X Pharmacy
Statement of Owner's Equity
Year Ended June 30, 19X7

Beginning Net Worth (7/1/X6)	$ 47,532.00
Add: Net Profit for Fiscal Year	35,363.00
	$ 82,895.00
Deduct: Owner Withdrawals for Fiscal Year	23,896.00
Ending Net Worth (6/30/X7)	$ 58,999.00

B. ADJUSTMENT PROCESS

One of the difficult areas of accounting deals with the transformation of recorded data for some time period (i.e., month, quarter, or year) into summarized data in the form of financial statements. This difficulty is further complicated in order to conform to the accrual basis of accounting. The transformation of recorded data takes the form of adjustments, also called adjusting journal entries. Their purpose is to update various accounts so that the financial statements are more accurate.

The adjustment process occurs at the end of the accounting period after all the transactions have been journalized and posted, but before the preparation of the financial statements. Each adjustment affects both a balance sheet account and an income statement account. Journal adjustments are made for items such as prepaid expenses, supplies, depreciation, and accrued items.

It is recommended that the recording of information be done by the pharmacy owner/manager, while the adjustment process and subsequent preparation of financial statements be done by a professional accountant. However, once generated, the financial statements should be used by the pharmacy owner/manager vis-à-vis *Lilly Digest* data for managerial purposes.

REVIEW QUESTIONS (III)

DIRECTIONS: Circle the letter corresponding to the correct answer for each of the following.

1. A financial statement that is time-static is the
    a. income statement.
    b. statement of owner's equity.
    c. balance sheet.
    d. both b and c.
    e. both a and b.

2. When the expenses for some time period exceed the revenues for that same time period, the pharmacy experiences a
    a. net income for the period.
    b. net loss for the period.
    c. break-even (no income or loss) for the period.
    d. none of the above.

3. The transformation of recorded data into formal financial statements includes
    a. adjusting the data to make the financial statements more accurate.
    b. comparing the financial statements to *Lilly Digest* data.
    c. hiring a professional accountant.
    d. both a and c.
    e. both b and c.

Check your responses on page 22.

IV. PAYROLL ACCOUNTING

A pharmacy's payroll consists of salaries and wages. Although the two terms are used interchangeably, there are technical distinctions. Salaries are usually based on monthly or annual amount, whereas, wages are normally based on an hourly amount. Full-time pharmacists and other full-time employees are commonly paid salaries, and part-time pharmacists, interns, clerks, and delivery personnel are often paid wages. The Federal Fair Labor Standards Act specifies the minimum level for wages and requires that any hours worked in excess of 40 hours per week must be at 1½ times the regular rate. The Act, however, does not apply to salaried employees.

It is important for a pharmacy to maintain adequate payroll accounting records of salaries and wages for a number of reasons. For example, federal, state, and local government agencies require employers to withhold taxes from employees' gross pay and to make timely payments of these withholdings. In addition, personnel costs represent the second highest expense of pharmacy practice, amounting to 19.4% of sales for community pharmacies and 11.4% of sales for chain pharmacies (the highest expense of operating a pharmacy is the cost of goods sold). Therefore, it is necessary to develop appropriate safeguards against overpayments, and improperly timed payments of payroll.

The payroll accounting system of a pharmacy is maintained for employees such as pharmacists, interns, sales clerks, stock clerks, and delivery personnel. Others such as accountants and lawyers, as well as the owner(s) of a pharmacy organized as a sole-proprietorship or partnership, are not paid through the payroll system. Instead of receiving salaries and wages, they are paid fees. The major distinction is that it is not necessary to withhold taxes from fees.

The net pay that an employee receives is gross pay less deductions such as federal income tax, Federal Insurance Contributions Act (FICA) tax, state and local income taxes, and, when applicable, contributions to savings and pension plans and union dues. The federal income tax usually accounts for the largest deduction. It is a graduated or progressive tax in that, as salaries and wages increase, the percentage paid in taxes also increases. The specific amounts of federal income tax that an employer must withhold are determined from tables found in the *Employer's Tax Guide* provided by the Internal Revenue Service. These tables are organized according to salary and wage ranges, payroll periods, marital status, and number of withholding allowances.

The Federal Insurance Contributions Act (FICA) tax, commonly called Social Security, is a regressive tax in that everyone pays the same percentage up to a maximum salary base. When the base earnings are reached in a given year, for a particular employee, the FICA tax is no longer withheld. If an employee changes jobs during the year, the new employer must withhold FICA tax regardless of the first employer. However, an employee who pays excess FICA tax will have it refunded when filing his tax return. For 1982, the FICA tax is 6.70% of gross pay up to $32,400.

The payroll may be disposed either through the pharmacy's regular accounting system and checking account or through a special payroll register and checking account. The special system, which provides better control, usually includes an earning card for each employee. Its purpose is to accumulate earnings data in order to generate tax information that must be provided to each employee and to determine when to cease withholding FICA tax. When the payroll for the period is completed, the column totals are posted to the appropriate accounts.

In addition to withholding the amounts from employees' gross pay, employers are required to set aside employer payroll taxes. These taxes are considered to be operating expenses and include FICA tax and federal and state unemployment compensation tax. As a guideline, such taxes approximate 10% of salaries and wages.

Employers are required to match the FICA tax paid by employees. The federal and state unemployment taxes are levied on employers only. They are computed in the same manner as the FICA tax, i.e., gross earnings are multiplied by the same percentage for all employees up to a maximum base. For state unemployment tax, the percentage and base vary for each state. In addition, variability may exist within a state based on the employment experience of individual employers. Generally, employers who provide steady employment are rewarded in the form of lower unemployment taxes.

REVIEW QUESTIONS (IV)

DIRECTIONS: Circle the letter corresponding to the correct answer for each of the following.

1. Which of the following individuals who have performed remunerable services for a pharmacy is **not** an employee?
   a. intern
   b. lawyer
   c. clerk
   d. both b and c
   e. both a and c

2. Which of the following is **not** withheld from an employee's gross pay?
   a. federal income tax
   b. state income tax
   c. FICA tax
   d. federal unemployment compensation tax

3. Which of the following is **not** a payroll tax levied against the employer?
   a. union dues
   b. FICA tax
   c. federal unemployment compensation tax
   d. state unemployment compensation tax

Check your responses on page 22.

V. USE OF PROFESSIONAL HELP

The basic business records for a community pharmacy consist of: 1) a recording system (which includes, at a minimum, the chart of accounts, the general journal, and the general ledger); 2) a periodic (at least annual) summation of data (which includes the adjusting process and the generation of financial statements); and 3) a payroll accounting system (which includes timely and accurate remittances of all amounts due to employees and taxing authorities, as well as timely filing of all required tax forms). Professionals such as lawyers, drug wholesalers, accountants, business form sales representatives, and representatives from data processing firms that specialize in payroll accounting should be consulted by a pharmacy owner/manager in the design and maintenance of the basic business records described above.

A. LAWYERS

A prospective pharmacy owner/manager, whether buying an existing pharmacy or starting a pharmacy from scratch, will retain a lawyer for the purchase and sale agreement and for the selection of an appropriate form of business organization. From prior experience, the lawyer may be in a position to make recommendations in the design of an accounting system or, at least, in the selection of an appropriate accountant.

B. DRUG WHOLESALERS

Similarly, the prospective pharmacy owner/manager will contact a supply source such as a drug wholesaler. In addition to being able to estimate a starting stock for a newly established pharmacy, a drug wholesaler may be able to make recommendations with respect to the design of the accounting system and/or selection of an accountant.

C. ACCOUNTANTS

As mentioned previously, an accountant should be retained in the adjusting process and subsequent preparation of financial statements. In addition, it is not uncommon to use this same individual to design the actual system of records, to be available (via telephone) to answer questions that may arise during the recording of information by the pharmacy owner/manager, and to demonstrate the various facets of the payroll accounting system, including remittances and filing of appropriate tax forms.

D. BUSINESS FORM COMPANY REPRESENTATIVES

Some business form companies, such as Safeguard Business Forms, have trained salespeople who can assist in the development of an accounting system for the pharmacy. They can determine the needs of the pharmacy and design an appropriate accounting system. Of course, their motivation is that the owner/manager of the pharmacy will use business forms, such as the general ledger or a payroll record card, that they manufacture.

E. DATA PROCESSING FIRM REPRESENTATIVES

Lastly, the payroll accounting problem can be delegated to a specialized data processing firm. Some of these firms, for as little as 50¢ per check, do the entire payroll accounting function including calculations, withholdings, timely remittances, and timely filing of all appropriate federal and state tax forms. As with business form salespeople, specialized payroll data processing representatives may be locally available.

REVIEW QUESTIONS (V)

DIRECTIONS: Circle the letter corresponding to the correct answer for each of the following.

1. Which of the following professionals would be able to assist a pharmacy owner/manager in the design of the system of records for the firm?
   a. lawyer
   b. drug wholesaler
   c. business form companies
   d. all of the above
   e. b and c only

2. Data processing firms are more likely to aid a pharmacist in which of the following pharmaceutical accounting area(s)?
   a. summation of data
   b. payroll accounting
   c. recording system
   d. all of the above
   e. b and c only

3. Which of the following professionals would be **best** able to aid a pharmacy owner in the adjusting process?
   a. lawyer
   b. accountant
   c. data processing firm representative
   d. business form company representative

Check your responses on page 22.

ANSWERS TO REVIEW QUESTIONS

I & II

1. d
2. b
3. b

III

1. c
2. b
3. d

IV

1. b
2. d
3. a

V

1. d
2. b
3. b

RECOMMENDED FOLLOW-UP

Readers who wish to expand their knowledge of basic business records for a community pharmacy may examine the following readings:

Internal Revenue Service. *Recordkeeping for a Small Business.* Publication 583. Washington, DC: Department of the Treasury, IRS, 1980.

Marion Laboratories. *Effective Pharmacy Management.* Kansas City, MO: Marion Laboratories, 1979. Chapter 2 of Section II.

Regan, R. C. *Financial Recordkeeping for Small Stores.* Small Business Management Series, No. 32, Washington, DC: S.B.A., 1976.

Siropolis, N. *Small Business Management.* Boston, MA: Houghton Mifflin Co., 1977. Chapter 11.

Tharp, C. and Lecca, P. *Pharmacy Management.* 2nd ed. St. Louis, MO: C. V. Mosby Co., 1979. Chapter 10.

POST-TEST

NOTE TO CONTINUING EDUCATION USERS

To obtain CE credit, remove the appropriate sheet from the accompanying answer sheet booklet and follow the directions for completing the post-test and applying for credit.

DIRECTIONS: Circle the letter corresponding to the **one** correct answer in each of the following.

1. Which of the following self-employed professionals should use the accrual basis of accounting for his practice?

    a. pharmacy owner/manager
    b. physician
    c. lawyer
    d. accountant

2. The recording of information process in a community pharmacy begins with

    a. the general journal.
    b. the general ledger.
    c. the chart of accounts.
    d. special journals and subsidiary ledgers.

3. All of the following are assets found in a typical community pharmacy **except**

    a. cash.
    b. accounts receivable.
    c. accounts payable.
    d. inventory.

4. All of the following are expenses found in a typical community pharmacy **except**

    a. repairs.
    b. delivery.
    c. sales.
    d. salaries and wages.

5. As transactions occur in a pharmacy, they should be

    a. posted and then journalized.
    b. journalized and then posted.
    c. posted and then adjusted.
    d. adjusted and then posted.

6. The accounting problems created by the sales cycle can be alleviated by use of a

   a. sales journal, cash receipts journal, and a subsidiary accounts payable ledger.

   b. sales journal, cash receipts journal, and a subsidiary accounts receivable ledger.

   c. purchases journal, cash payments journal, and a subsidiary accounts payable ledger.

   d. purchases journal, cash payments journal, and a subsidiary accounts receivable ledger.

7. The accounting problems created by the purchases cycle can be alleviated by use of a

   a. sales journal, cash receipts journal, and a subsidiary accounts payable ledger.

   b. sales journal, cash receipts journal, and a subsidiary accounts receivable ledger.

   c. purchases journal, cash payments journal, and a subsidiary accounts payable ledger.

   d. purchases journal, cash payments journal, and a subsidiary accounts receivable ledger.

8. Which of the following is a **minimum** basic record for an information recording system for a community pharmacy?

   a. sales journal
   b. cash receipts journal
   c. cash payments journal
   d. general journal

9. Because of their interlocking effect, financial statements are prepared in which of the following sequences?

   a. income statement, balance sheet, statement of owner's equity
   b. income statement, statement of owner's equity, balance sheet
   c. balance sheet, statement of owner's equity, income statement
   d. balance sheet, income statement, statement of owner's equity

10. A pharmacy has assets of $120,000 and owner's equity of $80,000. In the absence of other information, its liabilities are

   a. between 0 and $10,000.
   b. between $10,001 and $30,000.
   c. between $30,001 and $50,000.
   d. over $50,000.

11. A pharmacy has gross margin of $120,000, owner withdrawals of $15,000, and total expenses of $85,000. The pharmacy has experienced a net

    a. profit of $35,000 before owner withdrawals.
    b. profit of $35,000 after owner withdrawals.
    c. loss of $35,000 before owner withdrawals.
    d. loss of $35,000 after owner withdrawals.

12. Payroll taxes include all of the following **except**

    a. FICA tax.
    b. state income tax.
    c. state unemployment tax.
    d. federal unemployment tax.

13. Which of the following items should **not** be withheld from an employee's pay?

    a. union dues
    b. FICA tax
    c. state unemployment tax
    d. federal income tax

14. An employee has the following items withheld from his gross pay of $100.00: Federal Income tax, $10.00; State Income tax, $5.00; FICA tax, $6.00. In the absence of further information, it may be concluded that the employer

    a. is responsible for all three payroll items.
    b. is responsible for at least FICA tax.
    c. is not responsible for State or Federal unemployment taxes.
    d. is not responsible for any of the three payroll tax items.

15. All of the following professionals might be able to aid a pharmacy owner/manager in the design of the system of records for the firm **except** a

    a. lawyer.
    b. drug wholesaler.
    c. business form salesperson.
    d. physician.

NOTE TO OTHER USERS

The answers to the post-test are provided in the accompanying answer booklet for users who do not wish to obtain continuing education credit.

Unit Two

Management of the Community Pharmacy: Cash Flow

Jean Paul Gagnon, Ph.D.
School of Pharmacy
University of North Carolina at
Chapel Hill

TABLE OF CONTENTS

Study Time: **1,5 hours**
CE Credit: **.15 CEU**

INTRODUCTION

One of the responsibilities of a pharmacy owner/manager is to acquire and manage liquid assets, especially cash. This managerial function is extremely important, because having cash and putting it to work is a sign of a healthy, growing business. Insufficient cash, or lack of access to cash, can result in dire consequences, the worst being bankruptcy. During periods of financial instability and uncertainty, some owner/managers will seek outside funding to carry them through. Others see such times as a challenge and look within their businesses for innovative ways to increase the flow of money through the pharmacy's financial structure.

This program focuses on techniques that can be used to control cash flow within a pharmacy. It presents steps to be followed in order to minimize cash levels while maximizing the return-on-investment. Areas which will be discussed include: 1) differences between cash and income, 2) indicators and causes of cash flow problems, 3) tools for analyzing cash flow, and 4) techniques and guidelines for controlling cash.

OBJECTIVES

The objectives are presented here to aid the user in focusing attention on expected learning outcomes.

Upon completion of this unit, the user should be able to:

1. Make interpretive judgments regarding the financial management of a community pharmacy, given a sample cash budget.

2. Identify the signals and causes of business weakness.

3. Identify uses and requirements for the following:

   a. funds flow statement
   b. cash budget

4. Recognize strategies for improving the cash flow of a community pharmacy.

RECOMMENDED PREPARATION

This program is designed for pharmacy students and community practitioners interested in understanding cash flow management. The reader should be familiar with the uses and purposes of a balance sheet and income statement. He should have some familiarization with accounting terminology and should understand ratio analysis. It is recommended that the reader also review the following publications in conjunction with this unit:

Anthony, Robert N. *Management Accounting—Text and Cases.* 5th edition. Homewood, IL: Richard D. Irwin, Inc., 1975. Chapters 2 & 3.

Gagnon, J. P. *Management of the Community Pharmacy: Standards of Evaluation.* Chapel Hill, NC: Health Sciences Consortium, Inc., 1979.

Small Business Administration, A Handbook of Small Business Finance. Washington, DC: U.S. Government Printing Office, 1965.

I. SOUND CASH MANAGEMENT

A pharmacy's most liquid assets, cash and near-cash assets, are often its most current liabilities. While this paradox is strange to many pharmacists, the truth contained in it becomes more obvious each year. Cash shortages, because of rising interest rates and operating expenses, require owner/managers to examine their own operations in order to beat the "cash crisis." Although cash is used by many pharmacy owner/managers as a necessary cushion for unexpected demands on the pharmacy's resources, some owner/managers define cash as an asset upon which a reasonable return should be realized. These pharmacists know that they can improve their businesses by identifying trouble spots, trimming overhead costs, minimizing cash balances, and maximizing cash flow.

Cash is defined as, but not limited to, petty cash, paper money, coins, checks, cash waiting to be deposited, bank accounts, third-party forms, and credit-card receipts. Cash differs from income reported in the income statement in that part of a pharmacy's income from sales is cash and part may turn into cash in the near future. Thus, profits shown on an income statement and cash generated from operations are not identical. Because of lags in receiving cash payments and paying bills, coupled with the lack of proper cash management, it is conceivable that a pharmacy owner/manager can have high profits or income but insufficient cash to pay taxes.

Cash flow in a pharmacy exhibits some interesting properties. It is continuous and dynamic. Excesses in one month may have to be applied toward future months when applications are greater than sources. Because of the variability in cash flows, the pharmacy owner/manager must continually be apprised of future uses and sources of cash.

Management of cash requires understanding of the cash flow cycle, knowledge of factors affecting cash flow, and identification of indicators of cash flow problems.

A. CASH CYCLE

A pharmacy uses cash to purchase inventories and pay operating expenses (e.g., salaries, rent, utilities, etc.). Inventories, in turn, are sold for cash or credit. Credit is eventually returned to cash and, together with cash sales, is used to purchase new inventory and to expand operations. The primary problem associated with the cash cycle is that there are lag points. For example, if the wrong merchandise is purchased and/or receivables are not paid, cash may fail to materialize, and without cash, the business ceases to exist. Thus, the primary objective of the pharmacy owner/manager must be to accelerate this flow of cash in the cycle and to minimize the amount needed to run the pharmacy. Cash flow can be accelerated by addressing the lag points in the cycle and by reviewing the centers and services that use cash. The faster cash turns over, the less cash is needed to support the operation and, therefore, the higher the return-on-investment.

B. FACTORS AFFECTING CASH FLOW

Seasonal variation in inventory levels and receivables is one of the factors which affect the rate of cash flow in an operation. During some periods of the year, the rate of flow may decline, causing the pharmacy to experience a cash deficit. At other times, there may be cash surpluses that need to be invested in short-term securities. Other factors may include the terms of sale of pharmacy suppliers and the ability of the pharmacy owner/manager to identify an inadequate cash flow and, more importantly, to identify its cause(s) and the measure(s) to correct it.

C. INDICATORS OF CASH FLOW PROBLEMS

The first step toward understanding good cash management is the identification of the four indicators of cash flow problems. These include: 1) declining working capital, 2) stagnant or declining sales, 3) low profits, and 4) increasing debt.

1. *Declining Working Capital.* Working capital, i.e., the difference between current assets and current liabilities, should be adequate and liquid. In other words, sufficient cash is needed to pay expenses and meet contingencies. A pharmacy's working capital is inadequate if: the current asset to liability ratio, acid test, and bank balance are too low; trade discounts are not taken; and loan payments are delinquent. If any of these conditions exists, it could mean insufficient working capital and a cash flow problem. Possible causes of low working capital include: continual operational losses, unusual nonrecurring expenses, higher than normal expenses, over-investment in fixed assets, lengthening of the accounts receivable collection period, and slow-moving inventories.

2. *Stagnant or Declining Sales.* A leveling or decline in sales can have a pronounced negative effect on cash flow, because expenses may not decline in proportion to sales. Indicators of stagnant sales are: lower market share, sales increase at a decreasing rate, lower-than-average net sales to inventory ratio, customer complaints, and increases in the rate of return of goods. Causes of a decline in sales may be difficult to identify, but may include: satisfaction with the status quo, stocking of obsolete or unsalable items, failure to adopt new services, poor location, failure to monitor marketplace changes, poor pricing and marketing plans, and poor employee training.

3. *Low Profits.* Low profits result from declining sales, increased expenses, and/or increased cost of goods sold. The ratios that should indicate low profits include: the net profit to net sales ratio, the profit to tangible net worth ratio, and operating expense analyses. If these ratios are out of line with industry averages, the pharmacy may be confronted with a cash flow problem. Like stagnant or declining sales, low profits can stem from many areas, such as poor merchandising (pharmacy has an abnormal amount of unsalable items), poor organization, lack of long-term plannning, pilferage, or improper pricing.

4. *Increasing Debt.* The build-up of debt can adversely affect a pharmacy's ability to maintain an adequate cash flow. Unlike shareholders, debtors and creditors must be paid a fixed amount periodically. A pharmacy may have too many debts to take advantage of discounts. As a result, trade payables build up and the current liabilities to inventory ratio becomes higher than the industry average. High debt is usually the result of one or more of the following circumstances: over-investment in inventory or other assets, slow sales, increased expenses, owner withdrawing too much from the business, or inadequate owner investment.

In summary, a pharmacy owner/manager must constantly analyze his income and balance sheets using ratio analysis. In addition, he must identify and monitor indicators and causes of cash flow difficulties. Two tools that can further help identify cash flow problems are discussed in the next section.

REVIEW QUESTIONS (I)

DIRECTIONS: Supply the information requested in each of the following.

1. How is cash in a pharmacy's balance sheet different from income in the income statement?

2. Describe the cash flow cycle.

3. List four indicators that the community pharmacist should monitor for cash flow problems.

   a.

   b.

   c.

   d.

4. List four possible causes of stagnant or declining sales.

   a.

   b.

   c.

   d.

5. List four possible causes of low profits.

    a.

    b.

    c.

    d.

6. List four possible causes for increases in liabilities within a community pharmacy.

    a.

    b.

    c.

    d.

Check your responses on page 49.

II. FUNDS FLOW STATEMENTS AND CASH BUDGETS

Ratio analyses of a pharmacy's income statements and balance sheets provide much of the data necessary to assist a pharmacy owner/manager in the assessment of a pharmacy's operation. Two other tools that also provide valuable information to the pharmacist are the funds flow statement and the cash budget.

A. FUNDS FLOW STATEMENTS

The funds flow (sources and uses) statement explains changes that occur in an account, or group of accounts, during an accounting cycle. It describes the sources from which additional funds are derived and the uses to which these funds are allocated. It is constructed from an analysis of changes that have occurred in assets and equities between two balance-sheet dates for the purpose of appraising the soundness of the pharmacy owner/manager's decisions for shifting funds.

1. *Requirement for a Funds Flow Statement.* In a funds flow statement, sources equal uses, i.e., the sum total of all funds serving as sources of cash must equal the total of cash used by the business. Sources of funds for a business operation are generated from four areas: net profit, increased debt, decreased investment in assets (e.g., selling an automobile), and injection of capital into the pharmacy business structure by shareholders. Funds in a pharmacy operation are used when the owner/manager experiences a loss, pays a debt, purchases an asset, or withdraws funds from the business. It is important to remember that capital used to increase assets (e.g., purchasing a delivery car) or decrease liabilities (e.g., settling accounts payable) fall into the category of *uses*; freeing capital through decreases in assets (e.g., selling of a fixture), the addition of new capital through increases in liabilities (e.g., incurring a new debt), or increases in net worth (e.g., owner investing in the business) fall into the category, *sources of funds.*

2. *Construction of a Funds Flow Statement.* A funds flow statement is constructed from data in a pharmacy's beginning and ending balance sheets. Differences between balance-sheet accounts are used to construct the funds flow statement.

The first step in the construction of a funds flow statement is to arrange balance sheets in the report form as seen in Table 1. Once the two balance sheets are arranged side by side, one has only to calculate the differences between the various accounts and note whether the change was an increase or decrease.

The next step involves separating the account changes (noted in step one) into sources and uses of funds. The net result of this is the *sources and uses statement* as seen in Table 2. Analysis of Red Springs Pharmacy's sources and uses statement reveals a number of points about the pharmacy owner/ manager's behavior during 1980. The increases in accounts payable and retained earnings indicate the pharmacy is growing and the growth is being financed by reinvestment of profits. The increase in accounts payable is acceptable if sales have increased appreciably. Financing a pharmacy's growth through retained earnings is proper if the return-on-investment for these funds is greater than the present rate of return; otherwise, borrowed cash should be used to finance growth. The debt to equity ratio should be examined to see if it is too low or too high. To maximize the pharmacy's return on using these criteria for investment, the debt to equity ratio should be approximately fifty percent. The Red Springs Pharmacy owner/manager may have used the pharmacy's funds wisely to increase current and fixed assets in order to achieve the assets necessary to support sales growth. The levels of these assets should be compared to known standards (e.g., the *Lilly Digest*) for community pharmacies, to ensure that they are not out of line for a pharmacy with equivalent sales levels. It appears, on the surface, that the owner/manager of Red Springs Pharmacy is very astute and that the pharmacy is well-managed.

TABLE 1. Red Springs Pharmacy Balance Sheets

	1981	1980	(−) Increase (+) Decrease
Assets			
Cash	12,122	11,785	+337
Accounts receivable	25,426	24,171	+1255
Inventory.	62,425	59,391	+3034
Total current assets	99,973	95,347	+4626
Fixtures.	16,474	14,428	+2046
Delivery car	3,133	2,293	+838
Total fixed assets.	19,607	16,723	+2883
Total assets.	119,580	112,070	+7510
Liabilities			
Accounts payable	24,089	20,804	+3285
Notes payable.	7,070	7,070	—
Accrued liabilities	4,251	4,958	−707
Total current liabilities	35,410	32,832	+2578
Net Worth			
Common stock	6,000	6,000	0
Retained earnings	78,170	73,238	+4932
Total net worth.	84,170	79,238	+4932
Total Liabilities and Net Worth	119,580	112,070	+7510

TABLE 2. Red Springs Pharmacy Sources and Uses Statement
July 31, 1981

A. Sources of Funds

Increase in Accounts Payable 3285
Increase in Retained Earnings 4932

Total Sources 8217

B. Uses of Funds

Increase in Accrued Liabilities 707
Increase in Cash 337
Increase in Accounts Receivable 1255
Increase in Inventory 3034
Increase in Fixtures 2046
Increase in Delivery Car 838

Total Uses 8217

B. CASH BUDGETS

Because of lags in cash flow, it is important that the pharmacy owner/manager forecast cash inflows and outflows. One way to accomplish this task is to construct a cash flow budget. The cash budget forecasts, over a specified time period, all cash receipts and payments; it is a prediction of future cash flows based on an expected level of sales volume. A cash budget is a schedule of cash inflows and outflows over a period of time, for the purpose of pinpointing cash surpluses and shortages so that the pharmacy owner/manager may know when to invest or when to borrow. It is used to show when minimum cash balances have been reached, when the pharmacy needs to borrow, and when a debt can be paid.

The important points to remember about a cash budget are: 1) it is formed from sales forecasts and estimates of sales activities; 2) one must be careful to distinguish between the incidence of credit sales and the time of their collection, since a cash budget only recognizes cash receipts; and 3) an expense may not represent a cash disbursement (e.g., depreciation is not a cash expense).

The steps to be followed in constructing a cash budget are as follows:

1. *Determination of the Budgetary Period.* The period must be long enough to afford effective planning. If it is too short, the budget may fail to account for significant cash flows just beyond the last period. If it is too long, the chance of error is increased, and the time involved in preparing the budget is wasted. A six-month budget is acceptable in a community pharmacy, because it covers the major seasonal trends.

2. *Estimation of Sales and Expenses.* This is the most important step in constructing a cash budget. In forecasting sales, the pharmacy owner/manager must consider internal factors (e.g., previous sales history) and external factors (e.g., price changes, increased promotional activities or changes in the economy as they impact on sales). Expenses must also be forecasted based on the estimated sales level. The objective should be to project, as realistically as possible, the sales and expenses of the pharmacy over the next budget period.

3. *Calculation of Cash Inflows.* In this step, the pharmacy owner/manager calculates the pharmacy's net cash inflows or cash receipts, by month, for the next six months.

4. *Calculation of Cash Outflows.* After the cash receipts of the pharmacy are estimated for the budget period, the pharmacy owner/manager must estimate the cash outflows or disbursements.

5. *Calculation of Net Cash Gain or Net Loss.* The cash disbursements are subtracted from the cash receipts to calculate the monthly cash gains or losses.

6. *Calculation of Monthly Cash Balances.* Starting with the beginning cash balance from the most recent balance sheet, the cash balances for each month of the budget period are calculated by adding or subtracting the monthly cash gains or losses.

7. *Borrowing and Repayment Schedule.* The last step in the determination of the cash budget is the calculation of the total accumulative borrowing and excesses that the pharmacy will realize over the six-month period.

C. CONSTRUCTING A BUDGET FOR THE RED SPRINGS PHARMACY

The steps just described are illustrated in Tables 3-7 for the Red Springs Pharmacy. Before analyzing these tables, however, the following facts about this pharmacy's operation should be known:

1. Approximately 40% of the pharmacy's sales are credit sales. (It is located in a wealthier section of a southern town.)

2. Of the credit sales, 75% are collected in the first month following the charges, and 25% in the second month following the charges; there is no bad debt.

3. The gross profit margin on sales is 30%, thus, the cost of goods sold equals 70% of sales.

4. All inventory purchases are paid during the month of purchase.

5. A basic inventory of $62,000 is always maintained. The pharmacy's policy is to purchase adequate inventory each month to cover the following month's sales.

6. A minimum cash balance of $10,000 must be maintained, and accrued liabilities remain unchanged during the budgetary period. Additional financing from a local bank is available in multiples of $2,000.

TABLE 3. Sales and Expenses Forecast Through January

	Sales	Expenses
July	$17,000	$5,000
August	21,000	5,000
September	33,000	5,000
October	29,000	5,000
November	45,000	5,000
December	55,000	5,000
January	30,000	5,000

Rent 1300/month

Other Expenses .... 9% of sales/month

TABLE 4. Red Springs Pharmacy Balance Sheet
July 31, 1981

Cash	$ 12,122
Accounts	25,426
Inventory	62,425
Fixtures and Delivery Car	19,607
	$119,580
Accounts Payable	$ 24,089
Notes Payable	7,070
Accrued Liabilities	4,251
Net Worth	84,170
	$119,580

TABLE 5. Red Springs Pharmacy Cash Receipts

	June	July	August	September	October	November	December	January
Sales (forecasted for July-January)		$17,000	$21,000	$33,000	$29,000	$45,000	$55,000	$30,000
Credit Sales (40% of monthly sales)	7,600	6,800	8,400	13,200	11,600	18,000	22,000	10,000
Collections (75% of previous month's credit sales)		5,700	5,100	6,300	9,900	8,700	13,500	16,500
Collections (25% of credit sales two months hence)			1,900	1,700	2,100	3,300	2,900	4,500
Cash Sales (60% of monthly sales)			12,600	19,800	17,400	27,000	33,000	18,000
Total Monthly Cash Receipts			$19,600	$27,800	$29,400	$39,000	$49,400	$39,000

TABLE 6. Red Springs Pharmacy Cash Disbursement

Operating Transactions	August	September	October	November	December	January
Cash Receipts (from work sheet)	$19,600	$27,800	$29,400	$39,000	$49,400	$39,000
Cash Payments						
Purchases (70% of next month's sales).	23,100	20,300	31,500	38,500	17,500	21,000
Wages and Salaries	5,000	5,000	5,000	5,000	5,000	5,000
Rent	1,300	1,300	1,300	1,300	1,300	1,300
Other Expenses (9% of month's sales)	1,892	2,970	2,610	4,050	4,950	2,250
Total Cash Disbursements	31,290	29,570	40,410	48,850	28,750	29,550
Net Monthly Cash Gain or (loss) (receipts minus payments).	(11,690)	(1,770)	(11,010)	(9,850)	(20,650)	(9,450)
Cash Balance From Table 4 (end of month July 31, $12,122)	1,432	(1,338)	(12,348)	(22,198)	(1,348)	10,998

TABLE 7. Red Springs Pharmacy Budget

Financial Transactions	August	September	October	November	December	January
Cash Balance (beginning of month after financing)	$12,122	$10,432	$10,662	$10,348	$10,498	$10,498
Net Monthly Cash Gain or (Loss) (from operating transactions)	(11,690)	(1,770)	(11,010)	(9,850)	20,650	9,450
Cash Balance (before end of month financing)	$ 432	$ 8,662	$ (348)	$ (498)	$30,498	$19,948
Borrowing Required to Meet Minimum Cash Balance Requirements (multiples of $1,000)	8,000	2,000	10,000	10,000	(20,000) Repayment	(10,000)
Cash Balance End of Month After Financing	$10,432	$10,662	$10,348	$10,498	$10,498	$ 9,948
Cumulative Borrowing	2,000	10,000	20,000	30,000	10,000	0

An examination of the final budget (Table 7) for the Red Springs Pharmacy reveals that it will need to borrow money in the months of August, September, October, and November because of inadequate sales levels during these months. In December and January, the pharmacy's cash situation should improve dramatically. Using Table 7 and assuming that the sales forecast is valid, the owner/manager of Red Springs Pharmacy can borrow up to $30,000 over a four-month period beginning in August. He can retire the debt in December and January when he realizes a significant improvement in cash flow. To be more realistic and cautious, the pharmacy owner/manager might generate two budgets based on high- and low-sales estimates. Although it appears that the owner/manager of Red Springs Pharmacy has worked his way out of the current cash flow problem, he should investigate ways to speed up payment of receivables and increase sales levels. It also appears that inventory levels are too high; hence, purchasing behavior should be evaluated. It is obvious that the cash flow within the Red Springs Pharmacy needs better management. The following section addresses this problem.

REVIEW QUESTIONS (II)

DIRECTIONS: Supply the information requested in each of the following.

1. A cash budget is a schedule over time of a)_____
   and b)_____.

2. The cash budget is used to show when a)_____,
   b)_____ and when c)_____.

3. List the important points to remember in constructing a cash budget.

   a.

   b.

   c.

4. A short budgetary period may adversely affect a pharmacy because it fails to account for _____
   _____.

Check your responses on page 49.

III. STRATEGIES FOR IMPROVING CASH FLOW

So far in our examination of the Red Springs Pharmacy, we have concluded that the owner/manager has wisely used his funds, but that he does not have a complete understanding of the methods that can be used to improve cash flow. The owner/manager's objective, as far as cash flow is concerned, is to speed up the inflows and slow down the outflows as much as possible. This strategy has two benefits—it allows the owner/manager to invest less into assets, thus, increasing the pharmacy's return-on-investment, and improves its cash position.

When confronted with a cash flow problem, the pharmacy owner/manager must initiate a short-run plan for obtaining cash. Simultaneously, he should set into motion strategies that will improve cash position over the long run.

A. SHORT-TERM STRATEGIES FOR IMPROVING CASH INFLOW

When a pharmacy like Red Springs has a cash flow problem, the pharmacy owner/manager should take steps to accelerate the rate at which monies are received. In the short run, the owner/manager should focus on accounts receivable, inventory, some fixed assets, short-term investments and expenses, and other miscellaneous items.

1. *Accounts Receivable.* Accounts receivable are current assets that commonly reduce a pharmacy's cash inflow. Receivables should be examined to ensure that they are being paid within thirty days. An *aging of accounts report* needs to be constructed and used to identify delinquent accounts. If cash is needed immediately, delinquent accounts should be pursued. Slow payers should be contacted, and promises to pay by specific dates should be obtained. A form that collects previous credit history should be used for new accounts. To speed up payments, incentives, e.g., green stamps, may be utilized to encourage early payment of accounts. With the customers' agreement in advance, a percentage charge may be added on overdue accounts to stimulate payments. The thrust of accounts receivable management should be to accelerate payment of credit accounts.

2. *Inventories.* Inventories are also current assets that may reduce cash flow. A substantial amount of cash may be trapped in inventory. With the high carrying costs that exist today, a pharmacy owner/manager must maintain reasonably trim inventories. Computerized systems offer an ideal way to control inventories. However, many pharmacies cannot afford these systems and are restricted to manual types of control. Reviews of inventory using stock-record cards and dated stickers, although time consuming, can help reduce inventories. Moreover, an open-to-buy budget can be the one best method for controlling cash outflows in the short run. Products that have not sold within six months should be returned, if possible, to the pharmacy's suppliers. By limiting purchases and returning slow-moving items, the cash position of a pharmacy can be improved significantly.

3. *Other Strategies.* To obtain needed cash, in the short run, the pharmacy owner/manager may sell unused fixed assets (e.g., gondolas, etc.) that are collecting dust in the store's basement or attic. Sales promotions and/or

reduced prices can be used to rid the store of unreturnable inventories. Investments in short-term securities can be negotiated if cash is desperately needed. Overhead expenses should be scrutinized for possible reductions (e.g., comparison shopping for lower insurance). Other steps that the pharmacy owner/manager can take may include the following:

a. Place one person in charge of purchases (this will provide better control over inventories).

b. Place one person in charge of receiving merchandise.

c. Initiate specific short-term plans and objectives.

d. Evaluate services offered to consumers to ensure that such services generate revenues.

e. Tighten security to reduce pilferage.

f. Forego repairs or capital improvement.

g. Review the payroll to ensure that this expense is yielding a satisfactory return (non-cash bonuses, e.g., inventory or store gift certificates, can be used to conserve cash).

B. LONG-TERM STRATEGIES FOR IMPROVING CASH INFLOW

All of the short-term procedures for improving cash flow that have been discussed can be expanded and used over the long run. In addition, the following procedures should be implemented:

1. The owner/manager should examine his credit granting policy. A form that collects previous credit history from new/used ones should be used to determine suitable credit risks. Data collected on this form should be verified by contacting the listed references. A well-thoughtout form (many are available from banks or credit bureaus) can act as a deterrent to high credit risk patrons.

2. Over the long run, sophisticated inventory control procedures (e.g., computerized systems, and well-constructed open-to-buy budgets) can be implemented.

3. Fixed assets (e.g., buildings) can be sold or better utilized.

4. A sale and lease-back strategy might be employed to generate cash.

5. Accelerated methods of depreciation could be initiated with new assets (e.g., surgical appliances that are rented can be depreciated). Depreciation, although not a cash expense, can improve cash by reducing the amount of taxes to be paid.

6. Assets can be appraised to see if they have increased in value.

C. STRATEGIES FOR REDUCING CASH OUTFLOWS

The largest sources of cash outflow are accounts payable. The owner/manager should focus on taking advantage of the lags in paying bills for the purpose of slowing down cash outflow. Payment dates and terms of sale vary from supplier to supplier. The owner/manager should plan to pay his bills by the latest date possible yet still obtain discounts. An *aged statement of accounts payable* should be constructed showing the length of time of outstanding payments. A review of this statement will reveal which accounts can be postponed, thus, conserving cash in the short run. When the pharmacy is in a tight cash position, in the short run, the owner/manager may forego discounts and stretch out payments. The owner/manager should focus on the best time of the month to place orders. The objective should be to stretch out the payment periods for purchases as long as conceivably possible. This strategy can be effective in lowering cash requirements and, thus, increasing return-on-investments.

Assets are the other source of cash outflow. The objective of the owner/manager, in a tight cash position, should be to refrain from purchasing fixed assets.

In summary, the above strategies, if instituted over both the short and long runs, should improve a pharmacy's cash flow. The implementation and periodic use of funds flow statements and cash budgets will assist the pharmacy owner/manager in the proper management of the pharmacy. These aids, together with the use of techniques for improving cash flow, will allow a pharmacy to withstand any adverse economic situations.

REVIEW QUESTIONS (III)

DIRECTIONS: Indicate which of the following statements are true (T) and which are false (F) by circling the appropriate letter.

T   F   1.   The objective of the pharmacy owner/manager, in a tight cash flow situation, should be to slow down inflows and speed up outflows.

T   F   2.   The pharmacy owner/manager can positively affect his cash flow by following up the results of an aging of accounts report.

T   F   3.   An open-to-buy method of inventory control can be used to reduce inventory investment levels.

T   F   4.   Over the long run, cash flow can be improved by using accelerated depreciation methods.

T   F   5.   The largest source of cash outflow in a community pharmacy are fixed assets.

DIRECTIONS: Supply the information requested in each of the following.

6.   In the short run, a pharmacy owner/manager can improve cash flow by focusing on:

   a.

   b.

   c.

   d.

7.   Cash outflows can be slowed down, in the short run, by:

   a.

   b.

   c.

Check your responses on page 50.

ANSWERS TO REVIEW QUESTIONS

I.

1. Cash differs from income reported on the income statement in that part of a pharmacy's income from sales is cash, while part is credit.

2. Cash is used to purchase inventories and pay operating expenses. Inventories, in turn, are sold for cash or credit. Credit is eventually returned to cash, and together with cash sales is used to purchase new inventory and expand operation.

3. In any order:

    a.   declining working capital
    b.   stagnant or declining sales
    c.   low profits
    d.   increasing debt

4. Any four of the following:

    a.   satisfaction with status quo
    b.   keeping obsolete or unsalable products
    c.   failure to adopt new services
    d.   poor location
    e.   failure to monitor changes in marketplace
    f.   poor pricing and marketing plans
    g.   poor employee training

5. Any four of the following:

    a.   poor merchandising
    b.   poor organization
    c.   lack of long-term planning
    d.   pilferage
    e.   improper pricing

6. Any four of the following:

    a.   over investment in inventory or other assets
    b.   slow sales
    c.   increased expenses
    d.   owner withdrawing too much from the business
    e.   inadequate owner investment

II.

1. In any order:

    a.   cash inflows
    b.   cash outflows

2. In any order:

    a.   minimum cash balance has been reached
    b.   pharmacy needs to borrow
    c.   pharmacy can pay debts

3. In any order:

   a. It is formed from sales forecasts and estimates of sales activities.

   b. Distinguish between incidence of credit sales and the time of collection.

   c. Expenses may not represent a cash disbursement.

4. significant cash flows just beyond the last period

III.

1. F
2. T
3. T
4. T
5. F

6. In any order:

   a. collecting accounts receivable

   b. sales promotion and /or reduced prices to rid stores of unreturnable inventories

   c. cash in short-term investments

   d. scrutiny of overhead expenses

7. In any order:

   a. taking advantage of the lags in paying bills
   b. foregoing discounts
   c. postponing payment

RECOMMENDED FOLLOW-UP

Further information on cash flow management in a community pharmacy may be obtained by reading in the following sources:

Davidson, S. *et al. Accounting: The Language of Business.* Glen Ridge, NJ: Thomas Horton, 1975.

Duncan, D. and Herman, R. H. *Retailing: Modern Concepts and Practices.* Homewood, IL: Learning Systems, 1976.

Gitman, L. J. *Principles of Managerial Finance.* New York: Harper and Row, 1976.

J. K. Lasser Tax Institute. *How to Run a Small Business.* 4th ed. New York: McGraw-Hill, 1974.

Johnson, R. W. *Financial Management.* 4th ed. Rockleigh, NJ: Allyn and Bacon, 1971.

Magnus, N. and Hartman, P. N. *Accounting Essentials.* New York: John Wiley and Sons, 1972.

Thacker, R. J. *Introduction to Modern Accounting.* 3rd ed. Englewood Cliffs, NJ: Prentice-Hall, 1977.

Weston, J. F. and Brigham, E. F. *Essentials of Managerial Finance.* 3rd ed. Hinsdale, IL: The Dryden Press, 1971.

POST-TEST

NOTE TO CONTINUING EDUCATION USERS

To obtain CE credit, remove the appropriate sheet from the accompanying answer sheet booklet and follow the directions for completing the post-test and applying for credit.

DIRECTIONS: Circle the letter corresponding to the **one** correct answer in each of the following.

1. After completing the cash budget and cash requirements in Exhibits I and II (on the following page), what should the pharmacy owner/manager of Raquel's Pharmacy do?

   a. Nothing, there appear to be no financial problems.

   b. Contract to borrow $75,000 per month from a bank for the next 6 months.

   c. Contract to borrow up to $433,000 per month from January to May and pay back the loans starting in June.

   d. Reduce the minimum cash budget and increase monthly sales.

2. What could the pharmacy owner/manager of Raquel's Pharmacy do if cash flow was poor? (Also refer to Exhibits I and II to answer this question.)

   a. increase sales
   b. decrease expenses
   c. reduce purchases
   d. all of the above
   e. a and b only

3. Cash flow in a pharmacy provides the necessary funds to

   a. pay normal day-to-day expenses.
   b. purchase fixed assets.
   c. take advantage of special-purchase opportunities.
   d. all of the above.
   e. a and c only.

4. The funds flow statement is a useful management tool because it

   a. appraises the soundness of the decisions for shifting funds.
   b. tells what has become of funds obtained from various sources.
   c. tells what has become of net profit.
   d. all of the above.
   e. a and b only.

5. To construct a funds flow sources and uses statement you would need

   a. an income statement and a balance sheet.
   b. last year's and this year's balance sheets.
   c. last year's and this year's income statements.
   d. a cash budget and a balance sheet.

EXHIBIT I

Raquel's Pharmacy
Cash Budget for Six Months
January 1980 through June 1980

(Figures in Thousands of Dollars)

	Jan.	Feb.	Mar.	Apr.	May	June
Cash Receipts						
Collections from credit. . . .	$215	$245	$265	$385	$345	$ 505
Cash sales.	385	345	505	325	290	500
Total receipts	$600	$590	$770	$710	$635	$1005
Cash Disbursements						
Cash purchases	536	540	461	358	358	424
Salaries	146	131	192	124	110	137
Operating expenses	115	104	188	118	88	108
Total cash disbursements .	$797	$775	$841	$600	$556	$ 669
Net cash receipts (disbursements).	($197)	($185)	($ 71)	$110	$ 79	$ 346
Cumulative net cash flow . .	($197)	($382)	($453)	($343)	($264)	$ 84

EXHIBIT II

Raquel's Pharmacy
Analysis of Cash Requirements

	Jan.	Feb.	Mar.	Apr.	May	June
Beginning Cash Balance	$ 95	($102)	($287)	($358)	$248	($169)
Net Cash Receipts (disbursements).	(197)	(185)	(71)	110	79	346
Ending Cash Balance	($102)	($287)	($358)	($248)	($169)	$177
Minimum Cash Balance.	75	75	75	75	75	75
Cash Requirement.	$177	$362	$433	$323	$244	0

6. Which of the following is an indication of cash flow problems in a community pharmacy?

    a.   deterioration of working capital
    b.   rapidly increasing sales
    c.   declining debt
    d.   decreased frequency of returned goods

7. Given the following balance-sheet changes over 1980 for Lydia Pinkham's Apothecary, what changes can be used as sources of funds?

$ 3,000 increase in cash
$11,000 increase in inventories
$ 3,000 increase in depreciation
$11,000 increase in accounts payable
$ 6,000 decrease in notes payable
$ 6,000 increase in retained earnings

    a.   increased cash, increased accounts payable, increased retained earnings

    b.   increased cash, increased inventory, decreased notes payable

    c.   increased depreciation, increased accounts payable, increased retained earnings

    d.   increased cash, increased inventories, increased depreciation

8. Comparing the beginning and ending balance sheets for a pharmacy can be useful because the resulting analysis shows

    a.   where the pharmacy owner/manager obtained funds.
    b.   what the pharmacy owner/manager did with the funds.
    c.   change in the cash account from the beginning of the year.
    d.   all of the above.
    e.   a and b only.

9. The purpose of a funds flow (sources and uses) statement is to

    a.   measure a pharmacy's return on investment.
    b.   measure a pharmacy's liquidity position.
    c.   measure a pharmacy's net worth.
    d.   measure the soundness of the decisions for shifting funds.

10. In a funds flow statement, selling an antique fixture in a community pharmacy would be considered as a

    a.   source of funds.
    b.   means to increase assets.
    c.   use of funds.
    d.   means to decrease liabilities.

11. When a community pharmacy experiences a net loss during an accounting period, it experiences

    a. a decrease in net worth and, therefore, a use of funds.
    b. an increase in assets and, therefore, a use of funds.
    c. an increase in assets and, therefore, a source of funds.
    d. a decrease in liabilities and, therefore, a source of funds.

12. Which of the following are the most difficult and most important figures to obtain in preparing a cash budget?

    a. expenses
    b. accounts receivable
    c. sales
    d. costs of goods sold

13. The major reason for constructing a cash budget is to enable the pharmacy owner/manager to

    a. estimate net income for the next 6 months.
    b. control accounts receivable effectively.
    c. know how much to spend on merchandise.
    d. know when to invest and when to borrow.

14. Which of the following are sources of funds?

    a. increased liabilities
    b. decreased liabilities
    c. increased assets
    d. decreased capital funds

NOTE TO OTHER USERS

The answers to the post-test are provided in the accompanying answer booklet for users who do not wish to obtain continuing education credit.

Unit Three

Accounts Receivable Management in the Community Pharmacy

Robert H. Hunter, Ph.D.
College of Pharmacy
University of Cincinnati

TABLE OF CONTENTS

Study Time: 1.5 hours
CE Credit: .15 CEU

INTRODUCTION

Accounts receivable constitute one of the three major categories of current assets of the typical community pharmacy. It represents purchases made on credit from a pharmacy's patrons. Credit sales constitute between 20% and 50% of the total sales of the typical community pharmacy according to the 1980 *Lilly Digest*. The ability to manage accounts receivable can have a significant impact on the pharmacy's cash flow and its resultant liquidity.

The purpose of this program is to provide the owner/manager with basic information for establishing and monitoring a successful credit account program. This understanding should promote the development of sound accounts receivable management skills.

OBJECTIVES

The objectives are presented here to aid the user in focusing attention on expected learning outcomes.

Upon completion of this unit, the user should be able to:

1. Recognize the four types of "in-house" credit programs.

2. Recognize three areas of expense associated with any credit program.

3. Recognize the definition of "hidden opportunity cost."

4. Identify major areas of information that should be included on new credit account applications.

5. Recognize, from a monthly aged trial balance, the accounts status in terms of the pharmacy's accounts receivable "target" dollar amount.

6. Calculate the average accounts receivable collection period.

7. Identify credit program adjustments available that may alter the pharmacy's average accounts receivable collection period.

RECOMMENDED PREPARATION

In order to gain maximum benefit from this unit, it is recommended that the user have some background in pharmacy management or accounting. The following references will serve as additional preparation for this program.

Smith, H. A. *Principles and Methods of Pharmacy Management.* 2nd ed. Philadelphia: Lea & Febiger, 1980, pp. 313-314.

Marino, F. A., Zabloski, E. J., and Herman, C.M. *Principles of Pharmaceutical Accounting.* Philadelphia: Lea & Febiger, 1980, pp. 75-88.

Smith, H. A. "Financial Analysis and Control." *Effective Pharmacy Management.* Kansas City, MO: Marion Laboratories, 1979, pp. 158-159.

I. IMPORTANCE AND REGULATION OF CREDIT

The offering of credit is widely practiced by various retail establishments. The decision to offer credit, at least to low-risk patrons, is almost automatic in light of the general public's expectations and the nature of retail competition. Reports, such as the *Dichter Report,* confirm the belief that patrons of community pharmacies do have high expectations regarding the availability of credit and other service offerings. Independent community pharmacies have recognized these realities and generally do offer credit.

Meeting both the public's expectations and retail competition in regard to credit is an economic cost-benefit decision. Earnings in net profit derived from credit sales must be compared with the potential earnings from the monies tied up in accounts receivable at the going interest rates. The offering of credit does result in associated costs to the pharmacy. These costs, too, must be taken into account when the decision to offer credit is made.

A. ACCOUNTS RECEIVABLE

The current asset, in the form of accounts receivable, is of great financial significance. According to the 1980 *Lilly Digest,* 13% of the surveyed community pharmacy's assets, or 3.8% of its total sales, are in the form of accounts receivable. The trend over the past ten years indicates that accounts receivable, as a percentage of total sales, has been increasing steadily. This increase in accounts receivable indicates that credit sales have been growing in importance. Although this measure of liquidity is still relatively low for the average pharmacy, it is important to note that the data include operations which do not offer credit.

The importance of accounts receivable will vary according to the portion of sales made on credit. Typically, however, the accounts receivable to total current assets ratio shows a value of 13% to 17%, with lower values found in new pharmacies. This relationship merits attention. A slow but steady increase of accounts receivable to total current assets, which cannot be explained by deliberate actions or policy of the pharmacy owner/manager, might indicate that credit patrons are taking advantage of the pharmacy's credit policy. This may lead to rising uncollectible accounts and cash-flow difficulties. While some fluctuation in the accounts receivable balance is probable, the pharmacy owner/manager should be open to adjusting credit policies in order to keep receivables under control. As the 1980 *Lilly Digest* indicates, bad-debt write-offs accounted for 0.1% of the total sales of the average community pharmacy. Although this figure is relatively low, the dollars lost represent a drain on the net profit and cash-flow position of the average operation. This erosion of net profit is apparent if one considers that bad debts represent 4.9% of the typical community pharmacy's before-tax net profit dollars.

Lastly, as the use of third-party payment programs increases, more pharmacies that to date have not offered credit will begin to do so. While conscientious management of accounts receivable is of paramount importance, it should be noted that credit sales can represent a significant financial gain in net profit from patrons who may have not purchased from the pharmacy if they were not offered credit.

B. ESTABLISHING NEW ACCOUNTS

No cash management system can operate effectively unless careful attention is given to those to whom credit is extended and to seeing that payment is promptly made. Chances for collecting payment for anything sold on credit decrease as the interval between purchase and aggressive collection increases. A balance must be reached between overly conservative credit policies which may reduce bad debts, but lose profitable business by rejecting acceptable accounts, and overly generous credit policies which increase bad debts.

The system for developing new accounts must include: 1) a means to identify and contact potentially qualified applicants, 2) appropriate credit application forms, 3) a means to verify information obtained on the application forms, and 4) a means to advise the credit patron of the privileges and limitations of the account.

Notification of the credit terms, any service charges, products and/or services covered, the billing period, and credit-check mechanisms must be made by the pharmacy to any new credit patron. More importantly, and the critical step in controlling credit procedures, is the process of investigating the credit applicant. The credit application form should request all necessary data, including the following items:

1. Personal data: name, address, length of time the applicant has lived in the city, age, names of family members

2. Employment: employer, position, immediate supervisor, previous employer(s), name(s) of other employed member(s) of the family

3. Bank: the name of the bank(s) the applicant patronizes

4. Other charge accounts held

5. Credit references

A more detailed form may be developed similar to the sample credit application form found in the Appendix.

After obtaining the information, it should be verified through a credit bureau and a general credit report should be obtained prior to establishing a new account. It should be noted that a number of legal requirements regarding credit must be taken into account. While a full discussion of these requirements is beyond the scope of this unit, pharmacists will want to refer to the Federal Equal Credit Opportunity Act (PL 93-495) and the Federal Fair Credit Reporting Act (PL 90-321), and most certainly should obtain legal counseling before initiating a credit program.

Lastly, it is a good practice to issue an identification card to the approved credit patron and a letter describing the privileges and limitations of the credit program. It should be noted that a pharmacy's credit policies should not be so restrictive as to preclude the dispensing of a prescription on credit in an emergency.

REVIEW QUESTIONS (I)

DIRECTIONS: Circle the appropriate letter corresponding to the correct answer in each of the following.

T   F   1.   In making a decision to offer credit, earnings in net profit derived from credit sales must be compared with the potential earnings from the monies tied up in accounts receivable at the going interest rate.

T   F   2.   The pharmacist should issue an identification card to the credit patron after filing the credit application form.

T   F   3.   According to the 1980 *Lilly Digest,* 3.8% of the community pharmacy's total sales are in the form of accounts receivable.

4.   The credit application form should include information related to the applicant's

     a.   employment status.
     b.   credit history.
     c.   prescription needs.
     d.   all of the above.
     e.   a and b only.

Check your responses on page 74.

II. TYPES AND COSTS OF CREDIT PROGRAMS

The pharmacy owner/manager who is considering credit should evaluate several types of formal and informal credit arrangements, and the costs associated with extending credit.

A. TYPES OF CREDIT PROGRAMS

Once the decision to offer credit is made by the pharmacy owner/manager, the next decision to be made is the selection of the type of credit program(s) to be implemented.

1. *Formal "In-House" Credit Plans.*   There are four basic types of formal "in-house" credit arrangements. These include the ordinary open account, the installment account, the budget account, and the revolving account.

a.   *Open account.*   The most common type of credit used in pharmacy is the open account. It involves charging merchandise and services when purchased, with payment due when the bill is sent to the patron. The bills are usually sent at the end of the month in which the purchase was made. Until recently, pharmacies seldom charged an interest or service fee on delinquent accounts. Today, it is not uncommon for them to assess an interest/service charge of 1% to 1½% per month on the unpaid balance after the normal 30-day credit period has elapsed.

b.   *Installment credit plan.*   Although rarely used in pharmacy, the installment credit plan is applied for some expensive items such as hospital supplies. A down payment of 10% to 30% is collected, and the balance is paid in equal payments, usually monthly, over a period of 6 to 12 months. Again, an interest or service charge may be used under this type of credit arrangement.

c.   *Budget account.*   The budget account is simply a short-term modification of the usual installment plan. Normally, a larger down payment is required and the balance is paid in equal installments within a period of from two to four months. This plan is normally used for substantial purchases, such as wheelchairs. An interest or service charge may be used at the discretion of the pharmacy owner/manager.

d.   *Revolving account.*   This has been increasingly utilized, particularly by major department store operations. Community pharmacies have not used this approach appreciably, but some chain pharmacies are now using this method. The revolving account allows the patron to purchase up to a preset limit, for example $200, and the consumer pays a specified amount each month, for example $25 to $50. A service charge as high as 1½% per month is paid on the unpaid balance.

2. *Informal "In-House" Credit Plans.*   Two other types of credit are used by community pharmacies, but relatively infrequently. The "one-time" emergency account is available to the patrons to overcome momentary shortages of available cash to pay for needed products or services. The offering of this type of credit is solely at the discretion of the pharmacy owner/manager based on his goodwill and desire to be of service.

The other informal credit plan is the lay-away type. The patron pays a nominal amount to have the store hold an item to be purchased by a designated time. If the patron does not purchase the item or service by the agreed-upon date, he forfeits the initial payment. While relatively infrequent in community pharmacies, this may be used at Christmas time by some patrons.

3. *Third-Party Credit Arrangements.* The previous credit arrangements were controlled solely by the pharmacy owner/manager. Bank credit-card usage is on the increase in community pharmacy. Such credit arrangements introduce a third party into the credit policies and procedures. Any or all of the above credit plans are available from one or more of the various credit-card services. In every case, a service and interest charge, usually 1½% per month on the unpaid balance, is charged to the patron. With many of these plans, the pharmacy is charged a service fee of between 2% to 6%, usually based on the average sales for the type of store involved, to cover interest and collection costs associated with delinquent accounts. This service fee is in addition to possible membership fees, normally around $25, and a nominal, one-time printer fee if a credit-slip printer is used. The advantage of having much of the collection and other costs handled by the bank often outweighs the costs associated with offering bank credit-card arrangements.

A final note regarding bank credit-card arrangements. While these arrangements are a form of credit for patrons, they are not a part of the pharmacy's accounts receivable. Generally, credit-card sales receipts are submitted by the pharmacy to the card-issuing financial institution. The financial institution then automatically credits the pharmacy's account by the amount of the credit sale. Thus, based on the "guaranteed payment" to the pharmacy and on the rapid conversion of the credit sales receipt into cash, bank credit-card sales, while a form of consumer credit, are not part of the pharmacy's accounts receivable but can be considered a form of cash sales.

B.   COSTS ASSOCIATED WITH CREDIT SALES PROGRAMS

Control over credit sales is of major importance to community pharmacy. Not only does the pharmacy owner risk a bad-debt expense, but a tardy account reduces the pharmacy's net working capital: the residual of total current assets minus total current liabilities. Managers should realize that there are costs associated with the maintenance of accounts receivable. The investment in outstanding credit accounts reduces the funds available for other uses. This involves the "opportunity costs," which may be equated with the interest on short-term notes. This "opportunity cost" reflects the fact that money owed to the pharmacy for any length of time precludes the pharmacy owner/manager from use of these funds for that time in other ways such as short-term interest-bearing notes or accounts, or for reinvestment back into the pharmacy.

The extension of credit can be an expensive service. It is expensive in the amount of money lost from uncollectible accounts. Furthermore, past-due accounts can cause the loss of patrons who are embarrassed to shop where they have a delinquent account. In short, both hidden and obvious expenses exist when credit is offered.

While the hidden costs are somewhat uncontrollable, a number of costs associated with credit can be identified. They are 1) the personnel costs of establishing and maintaining credit policies and records, 2) billing costs such as supplies expense and postal costs, and 3) collection costs such as collection agency costs and/or telephone expenses associated with follow-up calls to delinquent accounts. The sum of these costs can constitute from 10% to 15% of the value of a pharmacy's accounts receivable.

Actions which can be taken to promote prompt payment of accounts receivable are available to the community pharmacy owner/manager. However, action taken, while perhaps resulting in payment, can lead to lost patronage if not handled diplomatically.

Every business needs a system whereby bills unpaid after the usual grace period are promptly followed by another bill with a notation that payment is now overdue. If the second bill remains unpaid, a third should follow after about three weeks.

A pharmacy owner/manager should not hesitate to use the telephone if the bill is long overdue. An account receivable not paid, at least in part, after three months should merit prompt action on the part of the owner/manager. Once it is suspected that the patron is stalling, stricter action is warranted. Depending on the size of the amount due, calling the patron personally, using a collection agency, or bringing in an attorney may be warranted. Under present interest and inflationary conditions, a pharmacy may lose as much as 1½% of the value of the bills each month if the monies owed remain unpaid.

REVIEW QUESTIONS (II)

DIRECTIONS. Circle the letter corresponding to the correct answer in each of the following.

T F 1. The open credit account involves charging merchandise and services when purchased, with payment due when the bill is sent to the patron.

T F 2. Bank credit-card arrangements are part of a pharmacy's accounts receivable.

T F 3. The budget account, which normally requires a larger down payment and a shorter payback period, is a modification of the usual installment account.

T F 4. Many bank credit-card programs charge the credit patron a service/interest charge, and also charge the pharmacy a service charge which typically ranges from 2% to 6% of the total credit sales made on the card program.

5. A pharmacy which offers a credit sales program can expect costs from the program associated with

    a. personnel costs.   c. collection costs.
    b. billing costs.   d. all of the above.

Check your responses on page 74.

III. MONITORING SALES CREDIT PROGRAMS

Providing sales credit programs necessitates monitoring accounts receivable, and dealing with bad-debt transactions and uncollectible accounts.

A. ACCOUNTS RECEIVABLE

There are two basic techniques of monitoring charge accounts: account age analysis and determination of the average collection period. However, before examining these techniques it should be noted that much valuable information can be derived from the charge account applications and individual charge records. Patron information found on the credit application can provide a base on which promotional mailings can be made. Individual charge records can aid in the determination of individual product movement, locating prescription numbers, as well as in the monitoring of the patrons' payments on account.

1. *Age Analysis.* A periodic age analysis (monthly, quarterly, or yearly) should be performed on outstanding accounts receivable, and accounts meeting the pharmacy's bad-debt criteria should be identified. It is critical for the owner/manager to develop appropriate criteria so that he may decide whether to place an account with a collection agency, take action personally to prompt collection, or write off the account as a bad debt.

The criteria should be based on real alternatives. Collection agencies usually charge 33 1/3% to 50% for collecting an account. The 50% rate usually applies to accounts which are less than $25, over one-year-old, or require the services of an attorney, or to situations in which an attorney has been retained by the client. The 33 1/3% rate applies to most other situations. The decision as to how delinquent accounts are handled need be made based on the pharmacy's desired reputation—as a firm, diligent collector, or an easy "mark." The former is, in all likelihood, a better choice since it applies only to bad debtors and not to other credit patrons.

Age analysis of accounts receivable provides a way to evaluate individual credit accounts by detailing the amount purchased, the amount paid on account, the amount carried forward, and the monthly balance—all on a month-to-month basis. An example of this technique is presented in Table 1. For the sake of simplicity, any interest/service charges involved in the account depicted have been excluded from the example. If such charges were levied by the pharmacy, they should, of course, be included in the age analysis computation.

By studying the age analysis of the patron's account, it is apparent that the owner/manager is in a dilemma. The patron has gradually fallen behind in his payments to the point that during the immediate past two months he has failed to pay even a small amount towards the balance due. After accumulating a balance of $110.00, the patron did not return during the most recent month either to pay on his account or to purchase on credit other items or services.

TABLE 1. Age Analysis of Account Receivable*

Credit Activity	Current Month	Prior Month	Second Prior Month	Third Prior Month
Amount Purhcased . . . . . $	0.00	$ 20.00	$50.00	$30.00
Amount Carried Over. . . .	110.00	90.00	40.00	40.00
Amount Due	110.00	110.00	90.00	70.00
Amount Paid	0.00	0.00	0.00	30.00
BALANCE.	110.00	110.00	90.00	40.00

*Modified version of Age Analysis table found in *Effective Pharmacy Management*, Marion Laboratories, 1979, p. 150.

This situation is common. It probably occurs because the patron is embarrassed about being behind in his payments. Appropriate communication with the patron by the pharmacy owner/manager, as early as the third prior month, may have eased or alleviated the problem. At this time, all that is left to do is investigate the nature of the charges, possibly to shed some light on the reasons for the overdue account. A large proportion of the outstanding balance due stemming from charged prescriptions may indicate that the patron is experiencing large medical payments due to illness in the family. Empathetic communication from the owner/manager may be appropriate as a first step in alleviating the patron's credit difficulties, and may correspondingly aid the pharmacy in collecting the amount due.

While the situation depicted in the age analysis is common, it could have been avoided, or, at a minimum, eased by more prompt attention paid to the account by the pharmacy owner/manager. For example, if the pharmacy, as part of its credit policies, had set a target level of outstanding balances due of greater than $100 or a target level of non-payment for any given month as the criteria to start more active methods of collection, the pharmacy could have taken steps as early as the second prior month. It was noted that in that month, while the outstanding balance was less than the target level of $100, no payment was made on the account. Likewise, if the target level was in terms of dollars outstanding, action would have been warranted based on the $110 outstanding balance in the first prior month. Target levels based on either dollars outstanding or time of non-payment can be a valuable addition to any community pharmacy's credit policy.

2. *Determining Average Collection Period.* The age analysis of accounts receivable is typically conducted on individual accounts. The pharmacy owner/manager can, however, expand the analysis to include all accounts receivable by determining the pharmacy's average collection period. Determination of the average collection period is a more time-efficient technique of monitoring all of the pharmacy's charged accounts. The computation of the pharmacy's average collection period is a useful endeavor in terms of the information it provides the owner/manager. The average collection period is a

measure of the amount of time required to collect the pharmacy's average credit sale and is calculated as follows:

$$\frac{\text{Outstanding Accounts Receivable}}{\text{Annual Credit Sales}} \times 365 \text{ days}$$

The outstanding accounts receivable figure is taken from the pharmacy's balance sheet and the annual credit sales figure can be found either from the pharmacy's income statement or from its charge sales records. An example of the computation of the average collection period follows:

> Annual Charge Sales   \$120,000
>
> Outstanding Accounts Receivable   \$ 10,000

1) \$10,000 ÷ 120,000 = .0833
2) 365 × .0833 = 30.4

or

1) \$120,000 ÷ 10,000 = 12, or the accounts receivable turnover
2) 365 days ÷ 12 = 30.4, or 30 days average collection interval

Since credit is usually granted on a monthly basis, a 30-day average is considered a reasonable period and meets the commonly accepted target level of days receivable. A period of up to 45 days is normally considered accepable; however, if the average collection period exceeds 60 days, the accounts receivable need immediate attention.

An accounts receivable collection period greater than 30 days indicates that those funds tied up in accounts uncollected are not available for regular operations or special purchases, and it could mean that the pharmacy is losing potential profit.

The average collection period must be viewed in connection with the pharmacy's average payable period. The pharmacy's average payable period is determined by the following formula:

$$\frac{\text{Average Payables to the Pharmacy's Creditors}}{\text{Purchases}} \times 365$$

If the average collection period exceeds the average payable period, it may indicate that the pharmacy will continually be required to pay its own trade creditors prior to collecting from its patrons. This situation could eventually result in a cash crisis and should be corrected early, before reaching the crisis stage. This problem is more acute for those pharmacies with large amounts of credit sales than for those pharmacies with relatively smaller proportions of total revenue derived from credit sales.

A pharmacy owner/manager may correct the situation by changing credit terms or by offering cash discounts for prompt payment by his patrons, thus reducing the collection period. Alternatively, he may attempt to negotiate longer credit periods from his suppliers. As a last resort, the owner/manager may try charging a finance charge on past-due balances in order to stimulate payment. State usury laws must be kept in mind, however, as well as the possibility of creating ill will among patrons.

A difficulty may arise when significant amounts of Medicaid or other third-party program receivables are present and reimbursement payments are lagging. Such a situation may seriously distort the average collection period. It is recommended that these receivables be segregated, if they are significant, for purposes of this analysis.

B. BAD DEBTS

The question of what constitutes accounts receivable in accounting terms must be answered before a community pharmacy owner/manager can effectively deal with any credit program. Accounts receivable represent the money owed to the pharmacy by charge customers, and include only those transactions which involve the sale of products and services in the pharmacy. If money is loaned out by the pharmacy, for example, the amount would be classified as a note receivable or some other accounting item.

The gross sales of the pharmacy are derived from cash sales and credit sales. Monies owed to the pharmacy as a result of credit sales and not collected by the pharmacy are classified as bad debts. The bad debts of a pharmacy are considered an expense of doing business and, therefore, are located on the income statement as an expense.

While a bad debt is based on monies the pharmacy knows it will not collect, there are two methods in accounting for dealing with these transactions: direct write-off or estimating methods. By the direct write-off method, an account is removed, in total, from the books at the time it is determined to be uncollectible. The bad-debts expense ledger is debited and the accounts receivable ledger is credited by the amount of the write-off.

The estimating method of bad-debts expense is based on either the historical uncollected accounts as a percentage of credit sales or as a percentage of receivables. If the percentage of credit sales is used, the method is known as the *income statement technique*. Conversely, if the percentage of receivables approach is used, the method is known as the *balance sheet technique*. In each method, an historically based percentage of uncollected accounts is determined from past financial statements. This figure, in terms of either a percentage of the credit sales or of the receivables, is then multiplied by the pharmacy's total credit sales or accounts receivable, respectively. The result then provides an estimate of the allowance for uncollectible accounts. This allowance for uncollectible accounts is a contra-account or offset account which reduces the assets, accounts receivable, by the amount of money estimated to be uncollectible. This contra-account is found under the accounts receivable notation in the current-assets portion of the pharmacy's balance sheet.

C. UNCOLLECTIBLE ACCOUNTS

Unlike a bad-debt expense, allowance for uncollectible accounts represents those monies the pharmacy projects will not be collected in a given accounting period. It does not indicate those monies the pharmacy has consciously given up collecting on. As an asset-reduction account, the allowance for uncollectible accounts attempts to place a value on the accounts receivable which is in keeping with the pharmacy's history of collecting accounts receivable.

REVIEW QUESTIONS (III)

DIRECTIONS: Circle the letter corresponding to the correct answer for each of the following.

T F 1. The decision to utilize a collection agency, take personal action or write off an uncollected account should be based on the pharmacy's desired reputation: an easy "mark" or a diligent collector.

T F 2. A credit account which exceeds the pharmacy's "target" level may either be above a predetermined dollar-amount outstanding and/or uncollected after a preset time period has elapsed.

T F 3. Account age analysis differs from the average collection period in that age analysis can **only** be conducted in a single account, whereas the average collection period can be determined for any number of accounts.

T F 4. A pharmacy with an average collection period of 45 days and a "target" level of 60 days for uncollected accounts receivable can be said to be managing its accounts receivable efficiently.

T F 5. Unlike bad debts (accounts which constitute an expense item on the business' income statement), allowances for uncollectible accounts are contra-accounts, which reduce the assets (accounts receivable) by an estimate of those monies which will not be collected in a given accounting period.

T F 6. Unlike bad debts, the allowances for uncollectible accounts are determined by an estimation method based on either past credit sales or accounts receivable.

7. Which of the following methods is/are used to monitor accounts receivable?

a. age analysis of accounts receivable
b. break-even point determination
c. computation of average collection period
d. all of the above
e. a and c only

8. An account receivable, an account located on a pharmacy's balance sheet, is a/an

   a. long-term debt.
   b. fixed asset.
   c. current asset.
   d. short-term liability.
   e. expense.

9. A bad-debt, an account located on a pharmacy's income statement, is a/an

   a. revenue.
   b. expense.
   c. contra-account.
   d. after-tax deduction.
   e. before-tax profit indicator.

Check your responses on page 74.

SUMMARY

The management of accounts receivable is essential to community pharmacies. Pharmacy owners/managers should encourage patrons to pay promptly. The average collection period, if continually exceeding the pharmacy's average payable period, may indicate an impending cash crisis. Immediate remedial action by the pharmacy owner/manager is imperative.

A pharmacy owner/manager may use a number of techniques to reduce the collection time of accounts receivable. The best inducement to ensure prompt payment may be the offering of discounts for payments received within the billing terms. The quick cash received by giving a small discount can often more than compensate for the collection costs associated with over-due accounts. Ideally, diligent accounts receivable management will result in low costs associated with collection and cash-flow optimization.

ANSWERS TO REVIEW QUESTIONS

I.

1. T
2. F
3. T
4. e

II.

1. T
2. F
3. T
4. T
5. d

III.

1. T
2. T
3. F
4. T
5. F
6. F
7. e
8. c
9. b

RECOMMENDED FOLLOW-UP

For further information regarding the management of accounts receivable, the user may read in the following references:

Huffman, D. C., Jr. "Establishing and Maintaining an Efficient Credit Sales Program." *Pharmacy Management,* NS 17(6):381-383, 1977.

Tharp, C. P. and Lecca, P. J. *Pharmacy Management.* 2nd ed. St. Louis, MO: C. V. Mosby Co., 1979, p. 1470.

APPENDIX I

A P P L I C A T I O N   F O R   C H A R G E   A C C O U N T

A	LIMIT	FILE	RES.

	DATE	TRADE	P. RES.
		EMPL.	H. BUS.
INTERVIEWER	PASSED BY	CHECK.	O.
		SPECIAL	N. NEAR
		REPORT	E.

MRS. MISS MR.	FULL FIRST NAME (PRINT)	INITIAL	LAST NAME (PRINT)	INITIAL	WIFE'S/HUSBAND'S NAME	INITIAL

ADDRESS — NO. & STREET — CITY — STATE — ZIP

OWN HOME ☐   RENT ☐   BOARD ☐

OCCUPATION & EMPLOYER — BUSINESS — ADDRESS — HOW LONG — INCOME

FORMER ADDRESS — HOW LONG

PREVIOUS EMPLOYER — ADDRESS

WIFE'S POSITION & EMPLOYER

AUTHORIZED BUYERS & RELATIONSHIP
1.
2.

SPECIAL INSTRUCTIONS - REMARKS

PLEASE LIST TWO RELATIVES AND ADDRESSES
1.
2.

BANK & BRANCH
1.
2.

CHECK
LOAN
CHECK
SAV.
LOAN

CHARGE ACCOUNTS — REG. INSTL.

TYPE OF ACCOUNT REQUESTED

REG. CHG. ☐
INSTL. ☐

APPLICATION FOR CREDIT

XYZ PHARMACY

I hereby make application for an account with XYZ Pharmacy in my name and the name of my spouse, who has authorized me to open said account. In consideration of the extension of credit to us, I agree to become personally liable for said account in addition to my spouse. I agree to pay all charges 30 days after the billing date shown on the monthly statement. It is further understood and agreed that a service charge of one and one-half percent per month will be assessed on balances delinquent for more than 120 days.

DATE _____ 19____   SIGNATURE _____

POST-TEST

NOTE TO CONTINUING EDUCATION USERS

To obtain CE credit, remove the appropriate sheet from the accompanying answer sheet booklet and follow the directions for completing the post-test and applying for credit.

DIRECTIONS: Circle the letter corresponding to the correct answer in each of the following.

T   F   1. The term "hidden opportunity cost," as it relates to poorly managed credit programs, means that monies tied up in uncollected accounts are not available to the pharmacy to invest in the business or in other investment alternatives.

T   F   2. In the establishment of any credit program, a pharmacy must develop a means to identify bad risks prior to including any patron in the pharmacy's credit program.

T   F   3. If a pharmacy has a target level of 60 days for accounts receivable and its calculated average collection period exceeds this level significantly, the pharmacy owner/manager can infer that accounts receivable are managed effectively.

T   F   4. The decision to utilize a collection agency must be based on the pharmacy's desired reputation as a firm, diligent collector and on the costs associated with the utilization of the collection agency.

5. All of the following are areas of expense, not including "hidden" expenses, associated with any credit program, **except**

   a. personnel costs.
   b. billing costs such as postal expenses.
   c. collection costs.
   d. service charge.

6. Credit application forms should request information pertaining to which of the following?

   a. personal data—name, address, etc.
   b. employment data—previous work experience
   c. credit references
   d. all of the above
   e. a & b only

7. All of the following are "in-house" credit programs available to patrons **except**

   a. ordinary open accounts.
   b. installment accounts.
   c. bank credit-card accounts.
   d. budget accounts.
   e. revolving accounts.

8. If a pharmacy's credit policies include a target level of $200 on overdue accounts, and the following age analysis was conducted on Mr. Jones' account, has the Jones account exceeded the pharmacy's target level during the first four months depicted?

    a.   yes   b.   no

Mr. J. Jones   Age Analysis of Accounts Receivable

Credit Acitivity	Apr.	Mar.	Feb.	Jan.
Amount Purchased	50.00	100.00	50.00	20.00
Amount Carried Over	165.00	65.00	25.00	30.00
Amount Due	215.00	165.00	75.00	50.00
Amount Paid	25.00	0	10.00	25.00
BALANCE	190.00	165.00	65.00	25.00

9. A pharmacy owner/manager who finds his accounts receivable collection period exceeding his "target" level may take which of the following actions in an effort to correct the apparent inefficiency?

    a.   write off bad debts quickly
    b.   offer cash discounts for prompt payment
    c.   negotiate shorter credit periods from his suppliers
    d.   accept fewer charge patrons
    e.   utilize a collection agency for all accounts past due beyond 30 days

10. A pharmacy's charge sales were found to total $150,000 for the past year. Its outstanding accounts receivable at the end of the past year were equal to $12,600. Based on these figures, the average collection period for the pharmacy for the past year was equal to

    a.   30 days.
    b.   35 days.
    c.   40 days.
    d.   45 days.
    e.   50 days.

11. A pharmacy owner/manager who wishes to reduce his average accounts receivable collection period may do so by which of the following strategies?

    a.   pay his creditors less frequently
    b.   renegotiate contracts with suppliers
    c.   offer cash discounts to promote faster payment by his credit patrons
    d.   all of the above
    e.   a & b only

NOTE TO OTHER USERS

The answers to the post-test are provided in the accompanying answer booklet for users who do not wish to obtain continuing education credit.

Unit Four

Inventory:
Its Total Cost and
Effect on Customer Service

Bruce A. Berger, Ph.D., R.Ph.
Assistant Professor
Behavorial and Administrative
Pharmacy
West Virginia University School of
Pharmacy

TABLE OF CONTENTS

Study Time: 1.5 hours
CE Credit: .15 CEU

INTRODUCTION

Inventory represents the largest asset investment in a pharmacy. Typically, over 50% of the funds of a pharmacy are invested in inventory. The ability to manage and control inventory can often determine the success or failure of a pharmacy.

The purpose of this program is to provide present and future pharmacists with basic information about the total cost of inventory and how customer-service decisions affect inventory levels. Understanding this information should promote the development of sound inventory management decision-making.

OBJECTIVES

The objectives are presented here to aid the user in focusing attention on expected learning outcomes.

Upon completion of this unit, the user should be able to:

1. Recognize the relationships between inventory levels and customer-service goals.

2. Identify the components of the total cost of carrying inventory.

3. Recognize the differences among the following terms:

    a. basic stock
    b. safety stock
    c. costs of inventory
    d. unit inventory control
    e. dollar inventory control

4. Recognize differences in channels of distribution with regard to procuring pharmaceuticals.

5. Recognize instances when the savings of buying drug products in bulk packages are greater than when buying small packages.

6. Recognize methods or procedures that aid in the systematic control and purchasing of inventory.

RECOMMENDED PREPARATION

In order to realize maximum benefit from this program, it is suggested that, prior to studying this program, the user read the following reference.

Zelnio, R. N. "Inventory Control Techniques." *Effective Pharmacy Management.* 1st ed. Kansas City, MO: Marion Laboratories, Inc., 1979, pp. 213-240.

I. OVERVIEW

Given the high cost of borrowing money and the overriding need to support sales while keeping inventory as low as possible, rational investment in inventory is not only necessary to hold costs down, it is essential for the survival of a pharmacy. Insufficient cash flow is the reason for most pharmacy failures, and the most pervasive cause of cash flow problems in pharmacies is inadequate inventory management.

The ability to provide service to customers is very much dependent upon adequate and proper levels of inventory. Inventory levels should be directly related to customer-service goals. If a pharmacy plans to carry a basic, competitive stock, plus specialty items that few others carry, the pharmacy must expect to have higher markup levels. In addition, a higher markup might be expected to compensate for slower stock turnover. The Gross Margin Return on Investment (GMROI) is called an "earn and turn" ratio. It measures the productivity of inventory relative to gross margin. Gross margin divided by net sales represents earnings based upon the selling of inventory. Net sales divided by average inventory represents a measure of inventory turnover. A standard range for this ratio is 150% to 250%. The example in Table 1 shows that, in order to achieve the same GMROI goal, Pharmacy A has to turn its inventory over more times than Pharmacy B, because Pharmacy A's markup is lower. Keep in mind that a pharmacy that has a good inventory turnover does *not* need to have a low markup. However, productive inventory *does* allow the pharmacy the flexibility to maintain a lower markup in order to be price competitive.

TABLE 1. Gross Margin Return on Investment (GMROI)

	$\frac{\text{Gross Margin}}{\text{Net Sales}}$	X	$\frac{\text{Net Sales}}{\text{Average Inventory}}$	=	GMROI
Pharmacy A	.30 (30%)		7		210%
Pharmacy B	.35 (35%)		6		210%

In addition to the most obvious reasons for controlling inventory (keeping costs down and improving cash flow and customer service), there are other important reasons for controlling inventory that should not be ignored.

1. Inventory control systems provide better record keeping for more accurate sales forecasting to provide for future customer needs.

2. Good inventory systems are less time-consuming for management. Once a system is set up, technical help can order and stock inventory. This frees the owner/manager to perform other necessary functions.

3. Good inventory control aids the pharmacy in promoting good relationships with suppliers. Ordering becomes more even and consistent. In this manner, suppliers can do a better job for the pharmacy. Good inventory control also cuts down the quantity of returned goods. This situation is good for both the pharmacy and its suppliers.

A. MANAGEMENT INVOLVEMENT

One of the purposes of this unit is to give pharmacy owner/managers the tools to be able to make sound inventory procurement and investment decisions. Management must develop the guidelines for properly ordering and stocking inventory. A good system works even when the owner/manager is not present in the pharmacy. Clerks and other technical employees can order and stock inventory based upon the standards set up by management.

B. THE "WANTBOOK"

Many pharmacists have a small notebook in which to write down items that are in low supply or out of stock. This notebook has been dubbed a "wantbook." Too often, pharmacy owner/managers use the wantbook as a substitute for systematic, planned inventory purchases. The only true justification for the wantbook is for customer requests of items not normally stocked. This unit should help pharmacists to move away from the use of the wantbook by providing several tools to aid in a systematic approach to inventory management. Inventory decisions may then be made based upon managerial expertise, not guesswork.

REVIEW QUESTIONS (I)

DIRECTIONS: Supply the information requested in each of the following.

1. List three areas that may be benefited by proper inventory management.

   a.

   b.

   c.

2. Name two activities that management should be involved in for proper inventory control.

   a.

   b.

Check your responses on page 98.

II. INVENTORY MANAGEMENT ISSUES

There are many costs associated with carrying inventory. Often, in making the decision to buy direct (versus through a wholesaler), the pharmacy owner/manager only considers the differences in invoice cost of pharmaceuticals, instead of the total cost of procuring and maintaining the pharmaceuticals ordered. Therefore, it is vital for the prudent pharmacy owner/manager to understand the total cost of carrying inventory and how these costs may be affected by where or how he chooses to buy goods.

A. COMPONENTS OF INVENTORY

There are two principal components of inventory. These are the *basic stock* and the *safety stock.* The basic stock is the amount of inventory carried to meet an average demand for the items stocked. The safety stock is that amount of inventory, above the basic stock, which is carried to meet an uncertain demand for an item. It also serves to counteract variation in order-cycle times that occur in replenishing inventory. The order-cycle time is the amount of time that elapses between when an order is placed to a supplier and when it is actually received. Knowing the order-cycle time for a manufacturer (or wholesaler) and the amount of variability it shows is critical in making proper purchasing decisions. Regardless of which channel (wholesaler or direct) pharmaceuticals are ordered through, the basic stock will not change. The safety stock will be affected, however. This will be discussed in greater detail in a later section.

B. TOTAL COSTS OF CARRYING INVENTORY

Before a discussion of channel considerations can be undertaken, a basic understanding of the total costs of carrying inventory is necessary. In order to measure the cost effectiveness of either channel, it will be necessary to understand the cost of ordering, carrying, and maintaining inventory. The costs of inventory include acquisition and order costs, and holding or maintenance costs.

   1. *Acquisition and Order Costs.*   These costs represent all of the costs involved in placing an order. These would include order preparation, communication of the order, and supervision of order placement. Of course, order preparation would include all costs associated with personnel needed to generate the order and to put it in the form that is necessary for its transmission or processing.

   2. *Holding or Maintenance Costs.*   These involve costs associated with carrying inventory. They include storage costs, property taxes and insurance, cost of capital, and cost associated with obsolescence.

      a. *Storage costs.*   These costs are not necessarily related to the total value of inventory. They are more product specific in regard to space allocation and special conditions, such as refrigeration and the like. However, it is not hard to imagine that these costs will go up as inventory levels rise. Moreover, if we are dealing with a limited or fixed amount of space, as inventory levels rise, we necessarily give up alternative uses for that space which may produce more income.

b. *Property taxes and insurance.* As components of maintenance costs, these are relatively self-explanatory. Inventory needs to be insured in case of fire, water damage, and the like. In addition, property taxes must be paid on inventory. Of course, both taxes and insurance increase with the level of inventory.

c. *Cost of capital.* This cost really deals with the question of how much money costs. Whether inventory is financed externally through debt or internally through revenues, there is a cost associated with using that money and tying it up in inventory. The cost involves a loss of alternative uses of that money for other investments. For the purposes of this unit, it is not as critical to understand the determination of the proper cost of capital as it is to understand the concept itself. That is, money has a cost. When investing in inventory, one has to consider the use for this purpose against alternative investments.

d. *Obsolescence.* Obsolescence deals with costs associated with the deterioration of a pharmaceutical over time. This can be due to a set expiration date, a new product that has replaced a given product, or damage to the product. Keep in mind that *depreciation* is not the same as obsolescence. Fixed assets such as a cash register or a delivery car are depreciated for tax purposes. Whether the pharmacy receives partial or full credit for a product returned to the manufacturer or wholesaler, there is a very real cost associated with returned goods: for the pharmacist's time, the vendor's time, and processing the returned goods. The pharmacy loses, even if the full price is obtained. The money previously invested was worth more yesterday than it is today. Money has a time value. A dollar today is worth more than a dollar in the future.

C. CHOOSING THE CHANNEL OF DISTRIBUTION FOR PHARMACEUTICALS

A primary consideration in choosing a source of supply for pharmaceuticals is the order-cycle time. The order-cycle time from the manufacturer to the retailer is, on the average, much longer than the wholesaler-to-retailer channel. Additionally, there is generally greater fluctuation or variation in order-cycle times from many manufacturers. Both of these factors should cause retailers to carry greater safety stocks. This, in turn, would cause an increase in total inventory costs due to increases in holding costs, capital investment, property taxes, storage costs, insurances, and possibly obsolescence.

In certain instances in which the order-cycle time is longer, it becomes necessary to make larger investments in inventory at one time to cover this period. The critical variable is the variation or fluctuation in order-cycle times. Table 2 illustrates this point. The average order-cycle time from two manufacturers may be 14 days. If manufacturer A varies by 10 days from the average, and manufacturer B varies by 2 days from the average, the effects on safety stock can be quite dramatic. In the second case, the retailer can be confident that a 14- to 16-day supply of stock will suffice. Manufacturer A's order-cycle time will vary anywhere from 4 to 24 days. Because of the larger variation and uncertainty, the retailer must order a safety stock supply of 24-days in addition to the basic stock to meet customer demands.

TABLE 2. Effects of Order-Cycle Time and Variability on Inventory Levels

	Manufacturer A	Manufacturer B
Average order-cycle time	14 days	14 days
Variation from average	10 days	2 days
Amount pharmacy needs to order till next delivery of goods (days supply)	24 days	16 days

Note: The pharmacy needs to order an extra 8-day supply from manufacturer A because of greater variability in the order-cycle time.

While manufacturers' direct prices are generally 15% below Average Wholesale Price (AWP), many wholesalers offer substantial amounts (10%) off AWP on pharmaceuticals for minimum orders (approximately $150). Manufacturers may also require minimums to achieve these discounts. Potentially, it may be easier to meet a wholesaler's minimum, because a retailer may place a single order that is a mix of pharmaceuticals from a multitude of manufacturers. Ordering direct would require many more orders, resulting in higher procurement costs. Minimums from a particular manufacturer must, by definition, consist only of the manufacturer's product line. In order to meet a manufacturer's minimum order, pharmacy owners/managers may order merchandise that does not move well or may order too much of an item that does move well, thereby tying up an excessive amount of capital at one time. It is estimated that it costs approximately 20% to 25% per year (or ½% to 1% per week) to carry inventory.* Based upon the previous information, it is not difficult to imagine that any differential in costs between wholesaler and manufacturer prices offered to retailers could easily be eroded by other costs associated with direct ordering. This is not to say that one should never order direct. Many manufacturers offer direct terms with low or no minimums with extremely short order-cycle times. The retailer should take advantage of these instances. The major consideration in choosing any vendor involves a comparative evaluation of three factors: order-cycle time, variations in order-cycle time, and minimum order required. All of these components can greatly affect the total cost of inventory.

Some other considerations are appropriate at this point. In making the decision to buy direct or through the wholesaler, the pharmacy owner/manager needs to consider the number of orders that must be placed, the number of credit terms that must be tracked, and the number of orders that must be checked in and put away when using either channel. In ordering direct, more terms of trade must be tracked from a multiplicity of manufacturers than if one or two major wholesalers were used. Additionally, the direct channel necessitates generating and receiving more orders than using a few wholesalers.

---

*VanDeMark, R. L. *Wholesaler Inventory Control.* Dallas: VanDeMark, 1977, pp. 25-26.

There are real costs associated with all of the considerations. Table 3 shows the relationship between procurement and carrying costs. In this example, it is most economical to order $120 worth of inventory three times per year. While pharmacists cannot be expected to know procurement and carrying costs for an order, the point is that procurement costs go up with each order placed while carrying costs go down. Carrying costs are directly related to the amount of inventory stocked. It seems reasonable to believe that the direct channel will not optimize the trade-off between procurement and carrying costs to yield the lowest total cost. The pharmacy owner/manager must trade off the difference in invoice costs between direct and wholesale purchase against the total costs involved in using the channel.

Finally, there are indirect costs or benefits associated with each channel that are not readily measurable. There are numerous services that wholesalers make available to retailers that are not offered by manufacturers. These services include inventory control, store remodeling and merchandising, same-day emergency delivery of pharmaceuticals, financial support, etc. This is not to discount the value of pharmacist-education programs provided by manufacturers. While there are costs associated with these services that are reflected in the cost of pharmaceuticals or in addition to the cost of goods, even if the total cost of inventory through the wholesaler is the same or not significantly different than the direct channel, the wholesaler channel may be preferred by many pharmacy owners/managers because of the service level.

TABLE 3. Relationship Between Procurement and Carrying Costs*

Value of Order	No. of Orders Per Year	Procurement Costs	Average Inventory	Carrying Costs	Total Costs
$360	1	$ 2	$180	$18	$20
180	2	4	90	9	13
120	3	6	60	6	12
90	4	8	45	4.50	12.50
72	5	10	36	3.50	13.50
60	6	12	30	3.00	15.00

*Modified from Smith, H. A. *Principles and Methods of Pharmacy Management.* Philadelphia: Lea and Febiger, 1975, p. 179.

In making the source-of-supply decision, it is not enough simply to look at differences in invoice costs. The other factors cited previously cannot be ignored. When these enter into the procurement analysis, the prudent pharmacy owner/manager may then choose a channel based on sound management decision-making.

D. BULK BUYING VERSUS SMALL-PACKAGE BUYING

Many times pharmacy owner/managers are faced with the decision of whether to buy a pharmaceutical in large quantity (a bottle of 1000 tablets) or in several smaller units (bottles of 100 tablets). When does the savings in bulk justify its purchase? Because bulk buying usually results in a lower cost per tablet (unit) to the pharmacy, the cost of goods sold will decrease. This means that the gross margin will increase. However, the turnover on the item will probably drop. When does the former justify the latter?

Given that it costs ½% to 1% per week to carry inventory, an example should help you in your decision-making. You have noticed from past movement that the drug Pharmacillin 250 mg moves 10 units of 100 tablets every 10 weeks, or one bottle per week. You know that a bottle of 100 tablets costs $5, while a bottle of 1,000 tablets costs $40. You save 20% on 1,000 tablets by ordering the larger unit. However, relative to the bottle of 100 tablets, it takes you 10 times as long to use the 1,000-tablet bottle at a cost of ½% to 1% per week. Even at this extra cost, you still don't use up the extra 20%, therefore, you should order in 1,000's. While the ½% to 1% per week figure is not an absolute, it is extremely useful in helping you to make good decisions about large or small unit ordering.

E. INVENTORY CONTROL AND CUSTOMER-SERVICE GOALS

As stated previously, pharmacy owner/managers must decide what their customer-service goals are. Relatedly, their store image needs to be decided. Both of these factors will have a substantial impact on inventory levels. Pharmacies cannot be everything to everyone. It is simply too costly. A pharmacy cannot be a discounter and full-service pharmacy at the same time. Full-service pharmacies need stock that has more breadth and depth than a discount pharmacy. Discount pharmacies need to turn their inventory more often to achieve similar profitability goals to broader service pharmacies.

Pareto's Law appropriately demonstrates the above points. Two correlates of Pareto's Law state that 20% of the pharmacy's clientele accounts for 80% of the sales, and 20% of the pharmacy's inventory provides 80% of sales. Table 4 gives an example of the effect of Pareto's Law on inventory levels. Inventory levels rise exponentially above the 80% in-stock level due to these relationships. To go from 80% in-stock to 100% in-stock, inventory levels would go up from $20,000 to $120,000. Generally, full-service pharmacies have a higher in-stock rate. Again, it is economically impossible for pharmacies to be everything to everyone. A pharmacy simply cannot afford to actively carry every item that customers request. This is especially true if a pharmacy decides to discount its merchandise.

TABLE 4. Pareto's Law (The 80:20 Rule)

	Time A	Time B
In-stock rate	80%	100%
Inventory level	$20,000	$120,000

Inventory levels rise exponentially above 80% in-stock level due to conditions expressed in Pareto's Law.

One way to alleviate the above dilemma is by realizing that an average in-stock rate is just that—an average. A pharmacy with an in-stock rate of 80% will have many items that are never out of stock (such as fast movers) and many items that are actively stocked far below this rate. Training customers to call in advance for low-demand merchandise is one way of keeping the inventory level low. This process is called "inactive" product stocking. The merchandise is only ordered when the customer places another order for it. In this manner, the customer gets the product he wants and the investment occurs only when the pharmacy is ready to dispense the product.

REVIEW QUESTIONS (II)

DIRECTIONS: Indicate which of the following statements are true (T) and which are false (F) by circling the appropriate letters.

T F 1. The amount of stock carried to meet an average demand is the basic stock.

T F 2. The basic stock fluctuates with order-cycle times.

T F 3. Cost of capital is not an actual cost of carrying inventory.

T F 4. Order-cycle times from manufacturers to retailers are longer than from wholesalers to retailers.

T F 5. The length of an order-cycle time is more important than its variability.

T F 6. It is **always** better to use the wholesaler-to-retailer channel than the direct channel.

T F 7. A pharmacy should only buy bulk packages direct.

T F 8. Inventory levels generally increase with customer-service levels.

Check your responses on page 98.

III. BASIC COMPONENTS OF CONTROLLING INVENTORY

In previous sections, reasons for controlling inventory were discussed. In this section, methods for controlling inventory are examined. There are trade-offs involved with each method. No inventory system is perfect, nor can it meet the needs of all pharmacies. However, this section will present you with concepts and ideas that will allow pharmacy owner/managers to modify the methods presented and adapt them to their particular pharmacy's needs.

A. UNIT VERSUS DOLLAR CONTROL

Before actual methods to control inventory are discussed, it is important to remember that the purpose of an inventory system is not to increase inventory turnover. The purpose of an inventory control system is to provide better customer service with lower costs. Inventory turnover should increase as a result, but it should not be our goal. Many times pharmacies have relatively good inventory turnovers but do not have the proper product mix to meet customer-service goals.

There are basically two types of inventory control: dollar control and unit control.

1. *Dollar Control.* Dollar control analyzes stock solely in terms of total retail dollar value. To accomplish dollar control, records are kept of the retail value of the inventory with little or no analysis of the determination of the proper number of units. Needless to say, dollar control is difficult to establish in the prescription department, where it is difficult to determine the retail value of prescription drugs before a given quantity is sold. Therefore, dollar control is more useful for outfront merchandise. The limitation to dollar control is that the method does not ensure the right mix of merchandise. It only allows a pharmacy owner/manager to determine if the budget set is being followed.

2. *Unit Control.* Perhaps a more useful inventory control technique for retail pharmacy is unit control. Unit control is used to maintain proper inventory levels by recording the quantities of inventory ordered and the rate of sale of individual items. Unit control is essential if the inventory manager is going to a) identify items that are selling best, b) invest properly in inventory, and c) use good buying procedures based upon inventory movement.

B. PLANNING INVENTORY LEVELS

It seems reasonable to assume that if units are controlled properly, dollar values for budgeting purposes will fall into place. The basic question is, how does a pharmacy owner/manager know how much to order?

Most computer inventory systems offered by wholesalers can determine order quantities for the pharmacy. But, if the owner/manager does not have a computer at his disposal and he can't afford a wholesaler's package, what does he do?

There are a few things all pharmacies should be doing, at the very least, that will increase the productivity of inventory.

1. All incoming inventory must be dated. At least the owner/manager will know how long the stock has been on the shelf.

2. A record must be kept of when the merchandise was ordered and how much.

The above items together will give the owner/manager a great deal of information about how long a lead time he needs in order to get the merchandise. Moreover, if the information is organized properly, he will begin to see a pattern of movement of the items in his inventory.

C. ORDER BOOK

One very useful method of organizing movement information is through the use of an order book. The order book will provide a written record of what was ordered, when, and how much. Table 5 is a sample order sheet in the order book. This particular inventory control system is based on unit control. It was developed to provide flexibility in inventory control. It may be easily adapted to large or small retail pharmacies.

The sample order sheet is divided up into several major columns. The first column contains the drug name, strength, package size, and dosage form. Since this system is concerned with unit control, the cost of the product is not listed. Spaces are also provided in the first column for new or additional products.

The next column, control number, is the key to the system. It designates how many full units or unbroken packages of the product should be on the shelf at any given time. The determination of this number is based upon two pieces of information: the desired turnover of the item and the number of units that turn over in the designated period of time. For example, if a pharmacy owner/manager wants an item to turn over 12 times a year, he needs a 4½-week supply (52 weeks/12 turns). Next, he needs to determine how many units turn over in 4½ weeks and to adjust this number for lead times and the like. The number of turns he desires is a management decision. An item that turns less than 6 times per year, that is, an 8-week supply, may not be actively stocked. A goal for the prescription department would be 8 to 10 turns per year. How does the owner/manager determine how many units turn in this designated time period?

After several weeks and months of ordering the owner/manager will begin to see a pattern of movement for each item. At that point, he may begin determining how much of the item moves in a designated period of time. The control number will be based on that movement.

If the pharmacy owner/manager is already receiving movement sheets or marketing reports from wholesalers, he may use them to determine the control number. The marketing report in Table 6 gives a description of the item, the monthly usage, and an average movement per month. The average monthly movement could be used as a control number for approximately one month's supply.

TABLE 5. Sample Order Sheet

Drug Name, Str., Size	Control No.	Order Dates 7/1	7/8	7/15	7/22				
ROCHE LABS CONT.									
Valium 2 mg tabs 500									
Valium 5 mg tabs 500									
Valium 10 mg tabs 100									
Valium 10 mg tabs 500									
Vi-Penta inf F drops									
etc.									
(new or additional									
Roche products									
go in these spaces)									
ROERIG LABS									
Antiminth susp 60 cc									
Antivert 12.5 mg tab 100									
Antivert 25 mg tab 100									
Atarax tabs 100									
Geocillin 250 mg tab 100									

TABLE 6. Sample Marketing Report

Item	Description	Year to Date	JAN	FEB	MAR	APR	MAY	JUN	JUL	AUG	SEP	OCT	NOV	DEC	AVG.
131	Actifed C Expectorant PT	94	3		1			1	1	1		4	3	2	1
227	Actified Tablets 1000	451	2		1			1	2	2	2	1	1	1	1
258	Adapettes 15 cc	133		6	12			6	12	6	12	12	6	12	7
277	Adapin Cap 10 mg 100	8		1											
288	Adapin Cap 25 mg 100	135	3		2			1	1	1	2	2		1	1

The sample order sheet shown in Table 5 is set up by company. The order book can be set up any desired way. In any case, it should be set up in a manner that closely resembles the way a pharmacy's inventory is set up, if possible. This will facilitate stock checking.

Once the control number is set, anyone can use the order book (the pharmacy owner/manager need not do the ordering). If for example, Valium® 5 mg 500's were being ordered, the person ordering sees a control number of 10. If there are four full units on the shelf, six are ordered. Control numbers should be reviewed every six to eight weeks for the following reasons:

1. *Changes in Seasonality.* For example, pharmacies need to reduce their antibiotic supply and increase their allergy medicine supply in the summer months. Neither of these items should remain high year-round; otherwise, this will unnecessarily inflate their inventory. For this reason, it may be wise to write control numbers in pencil.

2. *Adjustments in Inventory.* Making periodic adjustments in inventory allows pharmacy owner/managers to increase or decrease inventory levels on products, based upon past movement. New products sometimes replace older ones. As a result, a product that moved well in the past may slow down in the future. In addition, the demand for a product may increase, and the control number should be adjusted upward.

The system presented is not perfect. Modifications can be made to account for drugs that are shorted from suppliers. The system is proposed to give pharmacy owner/managers ideas about how to organize an inventory system. Any inventory system takes time before it can be truly effective and show results. Inventory must be tracked and monitored over time if no past records have been kept. This process may take a year to be effective. The system and its management must be dynamic and reviewed over time. Only then may reductions in inventory levels be seen, with increases in customer service as a result of having the right stock.

REVIEW QUESTIONS (III)

DIRECTIONS: Supply the information requested in each of the following.

1. List three reasons for controlling inventory.

    a.

    b.

    c.

2. Discuss the major limitation of the dollar method of inventory control in prescription departments.

3. Name three pieces of information that a good inventory system should provide.

    a.

    b.

    c.

4. List two reasons for reviewing control numbers every six to eight weeks.

    a.

    b.

Check your responses on page 98.

ANSWERS TO REVIEW QUESTIONS

I.

1. Any three of the following:

   a. cash flow
   b. customer service
   c. gross margin
   d. turnover

2. Any two of the following:

   a. developing guidelines for proper ordering
   b. developing inventory systems
   c. directing technical help in ordering merchandise

II.

1. T
2. F
3. F
4. T
5. F
6. F
7. F
8. T

III.

1. Any three of the following:

   a. improved cash flow
   b. improved customer service
   c. improved profitability
   d. better record keeping for more accurate sales forescasting
   e. good inventory systems are less time-consuming
   f. improved turnover
   g. better relationship with suppliers

2. Inventory is valued at its retail price using dollar control. Often, the retail price of an item in the prescription department is not known until a given quantity is sold.

3. Any three of the following:

   a. quantity ordered
   b. date ordered
   c. date received
   d. item ordered (size, strength, etc.)
   e. movement per period desired

4. Any two of the following:

    a. allows the owner/manager to make seasonal inventory adjustments

    b. allows the owner/manager to periodically increase inventory levels on products that move well

    c. aids management in reducing or eliminating products that are not moving well

RECOMMENDED FOLLOW-UP

Further information on the total costs of inventory and inventory control may be obtained from the following materials:

Bowersox, D. J. *Logistical Management.* New York: Macmillan Publishing Co., Inc., 1978.

Davidson, W. R. *et al. Retailing Management.* New York: Ronald Press Company, 1975.

Jackson, R. A. "Inventory Management." *Pharmacy Management,* 152(1):11-16 (Jan.-Feb.) 1980.

VanDeMark, R. L. *Merchandising to Maximize Your Margin.* Dallas: VanDeMark, Inc., 1976.

VanDeMark, R. L. *Wholesaler Inventory Control.* Dallas: VanDeMark, Inc., 1972.

POST-TEST

NOTE TO CONTINUING EDUCATION USERS

To obtain CE credit, remove the appropriate sheet from the accompanying answer sheet booklet and follow the directions for completing the post-test and applying for credit.

DIRECTIONS: Indicate which of the following statements are true (T) and which are false (F) by circling the appropriate letters.

T F 1. Full-service pharmacies generally have lower inventory turnovers than discount operations.

T F 2. Twenty percent of a pharmacy's inventory will serve 80% of its customers' needs.

T F 3. "Inactive" product stocking causes inventory levels to increase.

T F 4. Inventory levels tend to rise almost exponentially above the 80% in-stock rate.

DIRECTIONS: Given the information below, indicate whether each of the following is true (T) or false (F) by circling the appropriate letter.

You note from your inventory records that the drug, Bicycline 250 mg, moves 10 units of 50 tablets every ten weeks. You know that the wholesale prices to you for a bottle of 50 tablets and 500 tablets are $5.00 and $48.50, respectively. Assume that you can purchase either size bottle from your wholesaler and will receive delivery within one day.

T F 5. It takes nine more weeks to move a bottle of 500 tablets than a bottle of 50 tablets.

T F 6. It costs approximately 3% to 5% per week to carry inventory.

T F 7. It would behoove you to continue to buy the drug in units of 100 tablets.

DIRECTIONS: Match the appropriate term on the right column with its definition in the left. Write the letter corresponding to the correct answer on the blank provided.

____ 8. the amount of inventory needed to meet an average demand

____ 9. costs associated with the deterioration of a product

____ 10. the amount of inventory needed to meet fluctuations in customer demand

____ 11. the costs involved in obtaining money

____ 12. tracking the rate of sale of individual items in order to plan inventory levels

a. safety stock

b. storage costs

c. basic stock

d. unit control

e. acquisition costs

f. cost of capital

g. obsolescence

h. dollar control

DIRECTIONS: Circle the letter corresponding to the **one** correct answer for each of the following.

13. Which of the following is **not** a cost associated with carrying inventory?

    a. property taxes
    b. obsolescence
    c. depreciation
    d. cost of capital

14. Given the information on Pharmacy X and Pharmacy Y below, which of the following statements is **true**?

    a. Pharmacy X has lower inventory turnover.
    b. Pharmacy Y has a higher GMROI.
    c. Pharmacy X has a higher customer-service level.
    d. Pharmacy X has a higher GMROI.

	Pharmacy X	Pharmacy Y
Gross Margin	25%	35%
In-Stock Rate	85%	93%
Net Sales	$300,000	$300,000
Average Inventory	$ 50,000	$ 75,000

15. Which of the following statements is **not** true?

    a. The direct channel will generally cause procurement costs to be higher than the wholesale channel.

    b. The order-cycle time from manufacturer to retailer is generally shorter than wholesaler to retailer.

    c. There is greater variation in order-cycle times from manufacturers to retailers than wholesalers to retailers.

    d. It may be potentially easier to meet a wholesaler's minimum order than a manufacturer's minimum order.

16. Which of the following is **not** a method or procedure for systematically controlling and purchasing inventory?

    a. unit control
    b. the wantbook
    c. review inventory control numbers
    d. date all incoming merchandise

NOTE TO OTHER USERS

The answers to the post-test are provided in the accompanying answer booklet for users who do not wish to obtain continuing education credit.

Unit Five

Break-Even Analysis

Colman M. Herman, Ph.D.
Edward J. Zabloski, M.B.A., C.M.A.
Massachusettes College of
Pharmacy and Allied Health
Sciences

TABLE OF CONTENTS

Study Time: **1.5 hours**
CE Credit: **.15 CEU**

INTRODUCTION

The professional goal of practicing pharmacists is to provide their patients with quality pharmaceutical services at reasonable prices. To be in a position to accomplish this goal on a continuous basis, pharmacy owner/managers must earn a sufficient profit not only in the prescription department, but also in other sections of the pharmacy. One of the first steps in realizing this goal is the performance of break-even analysis, which considers the relationship of factors affecting profit. It may be conducted based on units, revenue, or time.

OBJECTIVES

The objectives are presented here to aid the user in focusing attention on expected learning outcomes.

Upon completion of this unit, the user should be able to:

1. Differentiate between variable and fixed costs.
2. Calculate a unit contribution margin for unit break-even analysis.
3. Determine a unit break-even point mathematically.
4. Calculate the amount of profit or loss based on unit analysis.
5. Determine a unit break-even point using a break-even graph.
6. Calculate the amount of profit or loss using a break-even graph.
7. Recognize the comparative advantages and disadvantages of mathematical and graphical unit break-even analyses.
8. Determine a unit break-even point using a profit-volume graph.
9. Determine the amount of profit or loss using a profit-volume graph.
10. Recognize the comparative advantages and disadvantages of break-even and profit-volume graphs.
11. Calculate a unit contribution margin for revenue break-even analysis.
12. Determine a revenue break-even point mathematically.
13. Determine a revenue break-even point using a break-even graph.
14. Recall the number of months in a fiscal year it takes for an average pharmacy to break even.
15. Recall the precentage range of total sales that is achieved in a fiscal year when the average pharmacy breaks even.

RECOMMENDED PREPARATION

The user is encouraged to read the following resources as preparation for the study of this unit.

Smith, H. A. "Financial Analysis and Control." In *Effective Pharmacy Management.* Kansas City, MO: Marion Laboratories, 1979, pp. 158-159.

Smith, H. A. *Principles and Methods of Pharmacy Management.* 2nd ed. Philadelphia: Lea & Febiger, 1980, pp. 325-327.

I. UNIT BREAK-EVEN ANALYSIS

The unit break-even point indicates the number of units of a product that must be sold if a pharmacy is to operate without a loss. Until this point is passed, the pharmacy is operating without a profit. The unit break-even point may be determined either mathematically or graphically.

A. MATHEMATICAL UNIT BREAK-EVEN ANALYSIS

To understand the concepts involved in this type of analysis, it is necessary to define some terms appearing in Table 1, which presents income statement data for the average *Lilly Digest* pharmacy. *Variable costs* are those that are not constant over time, but vary in proportion to sales. Conversely, *fixed costs* are those that are constant over time, not varying in proportion to sales. *Contribution margin* involves the expectation that a product should generate revenue in excess of its variable costs and thus earn a contribution to fixed costs and profit. In order to establish the unit break-even point, the unit contribution margin must first be calculated. This is done as follows:

Unit Contribution Margin = Unit Selling Price − Unit Variable Costs

Calculation of the break-even point involves a consideration of the unit contribution margin and fixed costs:

$$\text{Break-Even Point} = \frac{\text{Fixed Costs}}{\text{Unit Contribution Margin}}$$

At the break-even point, the profit is zero, i.e., the contribution margin is equal to the fixed costs, and the total revenue is equal to the total costs.

As an illustration, assume that a pharmacy has an average prescription price of $7, with a unit variable cost of $5, and total prescription department fixed costs of $50,000. Accordingly, the unit contribution margin would be:

Unit Contribution Margin = Unit Selling Price − Unit Variable Costs

$$= \$7.00 - \$5.00$$

$$= \$2.00$$

Thus, each dispensed prescription contributes $2 to cover the fixed costs and profit of the prescription department. The break-even point would be:

$$\text{Break-Even Point} = \frac{\text{Fixed Costs}}{\text{Unit Contribution Margin}}$$

$$= \frac{\$50,000}{\$\ 2.00}$$

$$= 25,000 \text{ prescriptions}$$

TABLE 1. Income Statement Data for the Average *Lilly Digest*
Pharmacy for the Year Ending December 31, 1979

Total Sales...........................		$391,681
Variable Costs		
Cost of goods sold..................	.$257,334	
Employees' wages	46,759	
Advertising.......................	4,436	
Bad debts charged off...............	565	
Miscellaneous.....................	10,362	
Total Variable Costs..................		319,456
Contribution Margin		72,225
Fixed Costs		
Proprietor's or manager's salary	25,346	
Rent............................	9,783	
Heat, light, & power.................	3,291	
Accounting, legal, & other professional fees ..	1,804	
Taxes (except on buildings, income, and profit) & licenses	5,848	
Insurance (except on buildings)	4,214	
Interest paid......................	2,584	
Repairs	1,344	
Delivery..........................	1,662	
Depreciation (except on buildings)	3,369	
Telephone	1,365	
Total Fixed Expenses..................		60,610
Net Profit (before taxes)...............		$ 11,615

Therefore, if the pharmacy dispenses 25,000 prescriptions, the prescription department will break even (see Table 2). If it dispenses more than 25,000 prescriptions, the department will earn a profit, and if it dispenses less than 25,000, it will incur a loss. Any profits will be equal to the number of prescriptions dispensed in excess of 25,000 multiplied by the contribution margin of $2. Similarly, any losses will be equal to the number of prescriptions dispensed below 25,000 multiplied by $2. For example, if 30,000 prescriptions are dispensed, the prescription department will be operating at 5,000 units above its break-even point and thus will earn a profit of $10,000 (5,000 × $2 contribution margin). Similarly, if only 20,000 prescriptions are dispensed, the prescription department will be operating at 5,000 units below its break-even point, thus incurring a loss of $10,000 (5,000 × $2).

TABLE 2. Profits and Losses for Various Quantities of Prescriptions

Number of Prescriptions	15,000	20,000	25,000	30,000	35,000
Total revenue ($7/Rx)	$105,000	$140,000	$175,000	$210,000	$245,000
Less: Variable costs ($5/Rx)	75,000	100,000	125,000	150,000	175,000
Contribution margin ($2/Rx)	$ 30,000	$ 40,000	$ 50,000	$ 60,000	$ 70,000
Less: Fixed costs	50,000	50,000	50,000	50,000	50,000
Net profit/loss (before taxes)	($ 20,000)	($ 10,000)	$ -0-	$ 10,000	$ 20,000

B. GRAPHICAL UNIT BREAK-EVEN ANALYSIS

Using the data from the previous example, the break-even point can also be determined graphically, rather than mathematically. For example, based on the data presented in Table 2, the number of prescriptions dispensed is presented on the horizontal or X-axis, while the dollars of revenue and cost are shown on the vertical or Y-axis (see Figure 1). The total revenues for the various quantities of prescriptions are plotted and then connected with a solid line. Similarly, the total costs for the various quantities of prescriptions are plotted and connected with a dotted line. The unit break-even point is found at the intersection of the two lines. (The value so determined, 25,000 prescriptions, is consistent with the results of the mathematical unit break-even analysis.) Profits are measured to the right of the break-even point and, at any point, are equal to the dollar difference between the total revenue line and the total cost line. Conversely, losses are measured to the left of the break-even point and, at any point, are equal to the dollar difference between the total cost line and the total revenue line. The graphical approach to break-even analysis may be easier to understand than the mathematical approach, but it is less accurate.

A profit-volume (P/V) graph occasionally is used in place of or in conjunction with a break-even graph. An example using the previous data is shown in Figure 2. The number of prescriptions dispensed is presented on the horizontal axis. Dollars of profit and loss are shown on the vertical axis, with a solid horizontal line separating profits (above the line) from losses (below the line). The profits and losses for the various quantities of prescriptions are plotted and then connected with a broken line. The break-even point is found where the profit and loss line intersects with the horizontal line. Figure 2 demonstrates that the break-even point is 25,000 prescriptions, which is consistent with previous results.

The profit-volume graph may be preferred to the break-even graph because, with the former, profits and losses at any point can be read directly from the vertical axis. However, the P/V graph does not demonstrate clearly how costs vary with activity. Break-even and profit-volume graphs often are used together in order to achieve the advantages of both formats.

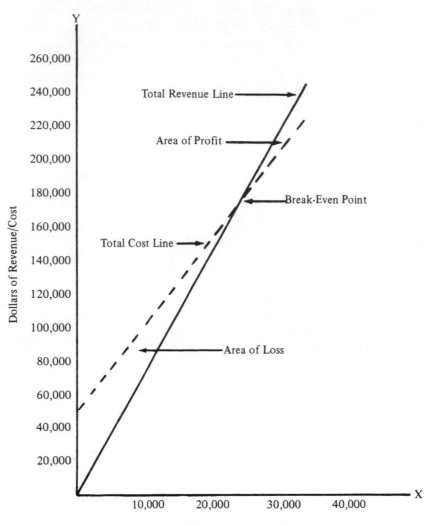

FIGURE 1. Break-Even Graph

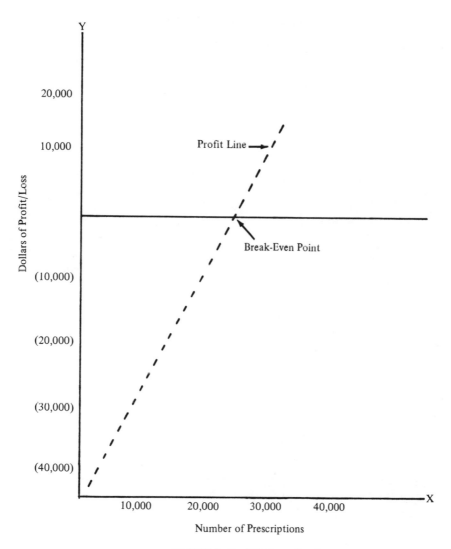

FIGURE 2. Profit-Volume Graph

REVIEW QUESTIONS (I)

DIRECTIONS: Circle the letter corresponding to the **one** correct answer in each of the following.

1. Costs that vary in proportion to sales are

   a. fixed costs.
   b. variable costs.
   c. total costs.
   d. costs for heat, light, and power.
   e. break-even costs.

2. Costs that do not vary in proportion to sales are

   a. fixed costs.
   b. variable costs.
   c. total costs.
   d. cost of goods sold.
   e. break-even costs.

3. With unit break-even analysis, the unit contribution is calculated as

   a. unit selling price — unit fixed costs.
   b. unit selling price — unit variable costs.
   c. unit fixed costs — unit selling price.
   d. unit variable costs — unit selling price.
   e. fixed costs — variable costs.

4. With unit break-even analysis, the break-even point is calculated as

   a. fixed costs ÷ unit contribution margin.
   b. variable costs ÷ unit contribution margin.
   c. unit contribution margin ÷ fixed costs.
   d. unit contribution margin ÷ variable costs.
   e. fixed costs ÷ variable costs.

5. Based on Table 2, what will be the profit or loss if the pharmacy dispenses 40,000 prescriptions?

   a. $30,000 profit
   b. $30,000 loss
   c. $40,000 profit
   d. $40,000 loss
   e. $45,000 profit

6. With a break-even graph, the unit break-even point is found at the intersection of the

   a. total revenue line and fixed cost line.
   b. total revenue line and variable cost line.
   c. total revenue line and total cost line.
   d. fixed cost line and variable cost line.
   e. fixed cost line and total cost line.

7. Based on Figure 1, what will be the approximate profit or loss if the pharmacy dispenses 10,000 prescriptions?

   a. $30,000 profit
   b. $30,000 loss
   c. $40,000 profit
   d. $40,000 loss
   e. $50,000 profit

8. In comparison to a graphical unit break-even analysis, a mathematical unit break-even analysis is

   a. more accurate, but more difficult to understand.
   b. less accurate, but easier to understand.
   c. more accurate and easier to understand.
   d. less accurate and more difficult to understand.

9. With a profit-volume graph, the break-even point is found at the intersection of the

   a. fixed cost line and horizontal line.
   b. variable cost line and vertical line.
   c. profit and loss line and horizontal line.
   d. profit and loss line and vertical line.
   e. fixed cost line and variable cost line.

10. Based on Figure 2, what will be the approximate profit or loss if the pharmacy dispenses 5,000 prescriptions?

   a. $30,000 profit
   b. $30,000 loss
   c. $40,000 profit
   d. $40,000 loss
   e. $50,000 profit

11. In comparing a profit-volume graph and a break-even graph, which of the following statements is(are) true?

   a. Profits and losses can be read directly from a profit-volume graph, but not from a break-even graph.

   b. A break-even graph demonstrates clearly how costs vary with activity, but a profit-volume graph does not do so.

   c. Profits and losses can be read directly from a break-even graph, but not from a profit-volume graph.

   d. a and b only.

   e. b and c only.

Check your responses on page 120.

II. REVENUE AND TIME BREAK-EVEN ANALYSES

In addition to determining the break-even point on a unit basis, it may also be calculated in terms of the revenue that must be earned in order to break even, or in terms of the number of months in a year it takes for a pharmacy to break even.

A. REVENUE BREAK-EVEN ANALYSIS

As with unit break-even analysis, revenue break-even analysis may be accomplished either mathematically or graphically and in a similar manner.

1. *Mathematical Revenue Break-Even Analysis.* The unit contribution margin and the break-even point are determined as follows:

Unit Contribution Margin (% of unit selling price) = Unit Selling Price (100%) − Unit Variable Costs (% of unit selling price)

$$\text{Break-Even Point} = \frac{\text{Fixed Costs}}{\text{Unit Contribution Margin (\% of unit selling price)}}$$

For example, using the data presented in Section I, the unit contribution margin would be 28.6%, calculated as follows:

Unit Selling Price	=	$7.00 (100.0%)
Unit Variable Costs	=	$5.00 (71.4%)
Unit Contribution Margin	=	$2.00 (28.6%)

Thus, the break-even point in terms of revenue would be:

$$\text{Break-Even Point} = \frac{\text{Fixed Costs}}{\text{Unit Contribution Margin (\% of unit selling price)}}$$

$$= \frac{\$50,000}{28.6\%}$$

$$= \$174,825$$

This means that the prescription department must generate $174,825 in revenue in order to break even. This is corroborated by the results shown in Table 2. The $175 difference is due to a rounding error.

2. *Graphical Revenue Break-Even Analysis.* The same graph (Figure 1) used for graphcal unit break-even analysis is used for graphical revenue break-even analysis. The revenue break-even point is found at the intersection of the total revenue line and the total cost line, the value being about $175,000. This is consistent with the result of the mathematical revenue break-even analysis.

B. TIME BREAK-EVEN ANALYSIS

The *Lilly Digest* presents a break-even analysis based on the number of months it takes in a year for a pharmacy to break even. The average break-even point for the 1,458 pharmacies submitting 1979 data to the *Digest* was 10.1 months, when 84% of total sales was recorded. Since 1970, the values have ranged from 9.5 to 10.1 months, when 79% to 84% of total sales was achieved.

REVIEW QUESTIONS (II)

DIRECTIONS: Circle the letter corresponding to the **one** correct answer in each of the following.

1. With revenue break-even analysis, the unit contribution margin is calculated as

    a. fixed costs (100%) — variable costs (% of fixed costs).
    b. unit selling price (100%) — unit fixed costs (% of unit selling price).
    c. unit selling price (100%) — unit variable costs (% of unit selling price).
    d. unit fixed costs (100%) — unit selling price (% of unit fixed costs).
    e. unit variable costs (100%) — unit selling price (% of unit variable costs).

2. With revenue break-even analysis, the break-even point is calculated as

    a. fixed costs ÷ variable costs.
    b. fixed costs ÷ unit contribution margin (% of unit selling price).
    c. variable costs ÷ unit contribution margin (% of unit selling price).
    d. unit contribution margin (% of unit selling price) ÷ fixed costs.
    e. unit contribution margin (% of unit selling price) ÷ variable costs.

3. With a break-even graph, the revenue break-even point is found at the intersection of the

    a. total revenue line and fixed cost line.
    b. total revenue line and variable cost line.
    c. total revenue line and total cost line.
    d. fixed cost line and variable cost line.
    e. fixed cost line and total cost line.

4. According to the *Lilly Digest,* the break-even point for the average 1979 pharmacy submitting data is

    a. 7.1 months.
    b. 8.1 months.
    c. 9.1 months.
    d. 10.1 months.
    e. 11.1 months.

5. According to the *Lilly Digest,* approximately what percentage of total sales was achieved at the break-even point for the average 1979 pharmacy submitting data?

    a. 54%
    b. 64%
    c. 74%
    d. 84%
    e. 94%

Check your responses on page 120.

SUMMARY

Break-even analysis may be performed based on units, revenue, or time. Whatever the basis selected, break-even analysis is a fundamental part of exercising managerial control. Specifically, it provides the pharmacy owner/manager with a valuable tool for the development of a profit plan, not only for the prescription department, but also for the other departments found in the pharmacy. The profit plan is then incorporated into the budgeting process.

ANSWERS TO REVIEW QUESTIONS

I.

1. b
2. a
3. b
4. a
5. a
6. c
7. b
8. a
10. d
11. d

II.

1. c
2. b
3. c
4. d
5. d

RECOMMENDED FOLLOW-UP

The following references can be read for further information on break-even analysis.

Marino, F. A., Zabloski, E. J., and Herman, C. M. *Principles of Pharmaceutical Accounting.* Philadelphia: Lea and Febiger, 1980, pp. 202-206.

Niswonger, C. R. and Fess, P. E. *Accounting Principles.* 12th ed. Cincinnati: South-Western Publishing Co., 1977, pp. 676-678.

POST-TEST

NOTE TO CONTINUING EDUCATION USERS

To obtain CE credit, remove the appropriate sheet from the accompanying answer sheet booklet and follow the directions for completing the post-test and applying for credit.

DIRECTIONS: Circle the letter corresponding to the **one** correct answer in each of the following.

1. Costs that vary in proportion to sales are

   a. break-even costs.
   b. accounting, legal, and other professional fees.
   c. total costs.
   d. variable costs.
   e. fixed costs.

2. Costs that do not vary in proportion to sales are

   a. break-even costs.
   b. advertising costs.
   c. total costs.
   d. variable costs.
   e. fixed costs.

3. The unit contribution margin is calculated as

   a. unit selling price — unit variable costs for unit break-even analysis.

   b. unit selling price (100%) — unit variable costs (% of unit selling price) for revenue break-even analysis.

   c. unit selling price — unit variable costs (% of unit selling price) for unit break-even analysis and revenue break-even analysis.

   d. a and b only.

   e. a and c only.

4. The break-even point is calculated as

   a. fixed costs ÷ unit contribution margin (% of unit selling price) for unit break-even analysis and revenue break-even analysis.

   b. fixed costs ÷ unit contribution margin (% of unit selling price) for revenue break-even analysis.

   c. fixed costs ÷ unit contribution margin for unit break-even analysis.

   d. a and b only.

   e. b and c only.

5. HSC Pharmacy has an average prescription price of $6.00, with a unit variable cost of $4.00, and total prescription department fixed costs of $40,000. The pharmacy's break-even point is

    a.   10,000 prescriptions.
    b.   15,000 prescriptions.
    c.   20,000 prescriptions.
    d.   25,000 prescriptions.
    e.   30,000 prescriptions.

6. Based on the data in question 5, what will be the profit or loss if the pharmacy dispenses 15,000 prescriptions?

    a. $10,000 profit
    b. $10,000 loss
    c. $20,000 profit
    d. $20,000 loss
    e. $25,000 profit

7. Based on the data in question 5, what is the pharmacy's approximate revenue break-even point?

    a. $100,000
    b. $110,000
    c. $120,000
    d. $130,000
    e. $140,000

8. The break-even point is found at the intersection of the

    a.   total revenue line and total cost line of the break-even graph for unit break-even analysis.

    b.   profit and loss line and horizontal line of the profit-volume graph.

    c.   total revenue line and total cost line of the break-even graph for revenue break-even analysis.

    d.   all of the above.

    e.   none of the above.

9. Based on Figure 1, what will be the approximate profit or loss if the pharmacy dispenses 5,000 prescriptions?

    a. $30,000 profit
    b. $30,000 loss
    c. $40,000 profit
    d. $40,000 loss
    e. $50,000 profit

10. In comparison to a mathematical unit break-even analysis, a graphical unit break-even analysis is

    a.   more accurate, but more difficult to understand.
    b.   less accurate, but easier to understand.
    c.   more accurate and easier to understand.
    d.   less accurate and more difficult to understand.

11. Based on Figure 2, what will be the approximate profit or loss if the pharmacy dispenses 10,000 prescriptions?

    a. $30,000 profit
    b. $30,000 loss
    c. $40,000 profit
    d. $40,000 loss
    e. $50,000 profit

12. In comparing a profit-volume graph and a break-even graph, which of the following statements is(are) true?

    a.   A profit-volume graph demonstrates clearly how costs vary with activity, but a break-even graph does not do so.

    b.   A break-even graph demonstrates clearly how costs vary with activity, but a profit-volume graph does not do so.

    c.   Profits and losses can be read directly from a profit-volume graph, but not from a break-even graph.

    d.   a and b only.

    e.   b and c only.

13. According to the *Lilly Digest,* since 1970, the break-even point for the average pharmacy submitting data ranged from

    a.   8.1 to 8.7 months.
    b.   8.8 to 9.4 months.
    c.   9.5 to 10.1 months.
    d.   10.2 to 10.8 months.
    e.   10.9 to 11.5 months.

14. According to the *Lilly Digest,* what percentage range of total sales was achieved at the break-even point for the average pharmacy submitting data since 1970?

    a.   67% to 72%
    b.   73% to 78%
    c.   79% to 84%
    d.   85% to 90%
    e.   91% to 96%

NOTE TO OTHER USERS

The answers to the post-test are provided in the accompanying answer booklet for users who do not wish to obtain continuing education credit.

Unit Six

**Nonprescription
Merchandising and Planograms**

Jeffrey A. Kotzan, Ph.D.
School of Pharmacy
University of Georgia

TABLE OF CONTENTS

Study Time: 1.5 hours
CE Credit: .15 CEU

INTRODUCTION

The sales and management of nonprescription (over-the-counter) merchandise can have a significant impact on the overall profitability of almost all pharmacy practices. Nonprescription sales account for approximately 50% of the total sales of traditional community pharmacies and approximately 80% of the total sales for promotion by discount pharmacies. Even pharmacies located in medical office buildings have a reported range of nonprescription sales of between 15% and 45%. Thus, it becomes apparent that nonprescription merchandising is an important area of concern for pharmacy management.

This unit is intended for use by pharmacy practitioners having management responsibility for over-the-counter or nonprescription merchandise. Additionally, this unit may be helpful for pharmacy students who are planning a career in community pharmacy.

OBJECTIVES

The objectives are presented here to aid the user in focusing attention on expected learning outcomes.

Upon completion of this unit, the user should be able to:

1. Identify the best selling location for a given department.

2. Identify two reasons for placing larger sized products to the right of the smaller products.

3. Recognize the best selling locations within a pharmacy.

4. Rank pharmacy goods in terms of the responsiveness of sales to shelf facings.

5. Recognize the stage of a product life cycle at which sales are most responsive to shelf facings.

6. Recognize the general guidelines for management of planograms.

7. Differentiate between the Bergen Brunswig and the Associated Druggist planograms.

RECOMMENDED PREPARATION

This program is intended for use by pharmacists and pharmacy students. Because of the basic nature of this material, no preparation is necessary.

I. PLANOGRAMS

Planograms are an important management tool for controlling over-the-counter (OTC) merchandise display. They are, as the name implies, plans for displaying OTC merchandise. They are structured on the basis of single-product categories such as analgesic-sedative or first-aid. A planogram indicates the appropriate number of shelf facings (i.e., the frontward and upright display of the primary selling surfaces of OTC products), and the placement on a specific shelf for each size of each product within a product category.

Planograms are available commercially from organizations which have access to national and regional sales figures on a product-by-product basis. These organizations compile the sales figures and construct the planograms on the basis of unit-volume sales and merchandising techniques. The major advantage for departments organized with the assistance of planograms is increased sales. Associated Druggist claims increased sales of 10% to 25% with the use of their planograms.

Two partial examples of typical planograms are presented in this program. The first is the SAM (Sales and Management Report) planogram, a product of Associated Druggist that highlights the important elements of the analgesic and sedative market (Appendix 1). This planogram defines three department sizes with estimated monthly sales, assigns the shelf facings and location for each of the analgesic and sedative products, and is accompanied by a picture of the department (not shown in this program).

The second, the Bergen Brunswig planogram, describes the first-aid department for linear shelf footages between 15 and 50 feet (Appendix 2). Reading from left to right, the number of shelf facings increase as the planned footage of the first-aid department increases.

The Associated Druggist planogram offers the advantage of providing a picture of the department, which makes it easier for the clerks to maintain the shelf facings to the specifications of the planogram. On the other hand, the Associated Druggist model is limited, in this case, to departments of either 72 or 36 linear feet. The Bergen Brunswig planogram is much more flexible, permitting department sizes between 15 and 50 linear feet. Therefore, it is easy for the pharmacy owner/manager to see when he or she should add or delete a particular size of a given product as the linear footage of the department is expanded or contracted.

The Associated Druggist planogram is, as stated previously, shown only in part. The planogram continues with alternative pricing strategies and marketing considerations for each department. The Bergen Brunswig model provides computer numbers for all of the planogram products, which greatly facilitates reordering.

Because planograms increase sales, they are excellent management tools for OTC pharmacy merchandising. Some pharmacy owner/managers may wish to implement either model wholly or in part. Others may wish to construct their own planograms. Knowledge of OTC merchandising techniques are important for those who wish to construct their own planograms or alter their purchased planograms.

II. NON-CONTROLLABLE OTC MERCHANDISING FACTORS

There are many considerations regarding individual product categories that are beyond the control of the pharmacist owner/manager. Foremost among these considerations is the conceptual framework of the OTC customer. How and why does a customer select a particular product? The consumer's decision process affects OTC merchandising and the construction of planograms because some product categories are more responsive to changes in shelf facings than others, despite overall unit sales.

A. PRODUCT CATEGORIES

Most OTC drug products are classified as convenience goods; that is, those products for which the customer is not willing to spend a great deal of time and effort comparing quality, performance, and price. As is true for the great majority of OTC merchandise, convenience goods have small unit prices. There are three types of convenience goods based upon the consumer's consideration of a single product at a single point in time: staple purchases, emergency purchases, and impulse purchases.

1. *Staple Purchases.* Staple purchases are bought routinely, without much thought beyond the initial decision to buy. Staple goods are purchased frequently on the basis of brand recognition; thus, display is of modest importance. For example, a customer may realize that he is out of aspirin and stop on the way home from work to pick up a bottle of Bayer Aspirin®. He can immediately find the brand sought because Bayer Aspirin® receives prominent shelf location and adequate shelf facings.

2. *Emergency Purchases.* Emergency purchases are urgent and are purchased without much consideration of price and quality. For a person acutely suffering from a toothache, for example, the purchase of toothache drops is classified as an emergency purchase. Shelf facings and display are not essential for emergency purchases.

3. *Impulse Purchases.* These purchases are unplanned before entering the pharmacy and are initiated upon sight of a particular product. Obviously, the purchase of impulse items is greatly dependent upon the merchandise display and shelf facings. When considering the fact that as much as 40% of the total of OTC purchases are impulsive purchases, one can easily see the significance of OTC display and the effect of management decisions upon total OTC sales. The pharmacy owner/manager must decide which categories of products are most likely to be purchased impulsively and which should be considered staples. He should give a prominent location to impulse items and should maximize the shelf facings of the national sales leaders at the most prominent location within the category display.

B. MARKET MATURITY

Factors other than those associated with the consumer's decision process also affect the responsiveness of sales to shelf facings and product location. Generally, those products in the introductory stage of market maturity will benefit most from increased shelf facings. New products or old products with new colors, flavors, etc. are generally considered in the introductory stage of market maturity. The responsiveness of sales to shelf facings may, in part, be associated with the heavy promotional effort which accompanies most product introductions.

C. SEASONAL PRODUCTS

Certainly, the pharmacy owner/manager must think in terms of the "seasonableness" of a given product category. During the colder months when coughs and colds are the heaviest, expansion of the entire cold-product category will significantly increase sales. On the surface, it may appear that the work of expanding sections is not worth the additional incremental sales; however, some owner/managers have gone so far as to move entire product sections with a resulting dramatic increase in sales. Some departments will be drastically altered or totally removed and replaced from season to season. Suntan products, Christmas candy, and Easter cards are examples.

D. PATRONAGE

Types of patronage also influence the responsiveness of sales to merchandising manipulations. A pharmacy serving predominantly retired people on small, fixed incomes cannot expect greatly increased sales from altered arrangements of the OTC inventory. An elderly person existing on a fixed income in inflationary times does not have the discretionary income available to purchase impulse items. A pharmacy serving a young married population will naturally increase the amount of shelf space devoted to baby needs and can expect increased sales from proper management of that department.

E. INTERPRODUCT COMPETITION

Competitive factors are a further consideration in shelf space allocations and product placement. A product category that is highly competitive on a national scale, such as the analgesics, can be greatly affected by shelf space management. Since the consumer is aware of the competing brand names and is constantly reminded of the brands through promotion, the brand receiving the maximum shelf exposure will appear most attractive to the consumer, and will generate more sales. Hence, the product which is the national or regional sales leader should receive the maximum shelf exposure.

F. COMPETITION FROM RETAILERS

Competition from other pharmacies and general merchandisers, such as discount and grocery stores, should also be a consideration in the management of OTC merchandise. Mass merchandisers provide maximum display for the leading brands. Physical proximity of mass merchandisers will diminish the relationship between sales and shelf facings of leading brands for pharmacy OTC merchandise.

G. MERCHANDISING TECHNIQUES

Special display techniques, other than shelf facings and location, may be employed to increase sales further. These techniques are both inexpensive (in some cases, free) and highly effective in stimulating sales. Pharmacy owner/managers should be particularly cognizant of the powerful effect of these techniques.

1. *Shelf or Channel Strips.*   A shelf strip or channel strip is a successful means of calling attention to a particular product. The strip fits into the price channel on conventional shelving and can be used to advertise price or simply call attention to a particular product.

2. *Shelf Extenders.*   A shelf extender is a package which is set out beyond the shelf by a couple of inches and is used as another means of increasing sales of the individual product.

3. *Product Spotter.*   The idea of a product spotter is similar to that of the shelf extender, in that the spotter sits several inches beyond the shelf. The product spotter is usually a plastic device that fits underneath the product container and simply calls attention to the product location.

4. *Display Cartons.*   Many products come pre-packaged in display cartons for immediate placement in inventory. Display cartons are an inexpensive and highly effective means of increasing sales of individual products.

5. *Package Talkers.*   Another means of increasing sales is a package talker, that is, a special message contained on the usual package. An example of a package-talker message is "new improved formula" or "free sample enclosed."

REVIEW QUESTIONS (I & II)

DIRECTIONS: Circle the appropriate letter or supply the information requested in each of the following.

T   F   1.   An advantage of the Associated Druggist planogram is the provision of a picture of the department.

T   F   2.   A pharmacy serving predominantly retired people on small, fixed incomes can expect a large increase in sales from altered arrangement of the OTC inventory.

T   F   3.   Physical proximity of mass merchandisers will diminish the relationship between sales and shelf facings of leading brands for pharmacy OTC merchandise.

4.   A product spotter is

   a.   a special message contained on a package.
   b.   a free display carton.
   c.   set out beyond the shelf a couple of inches.
   d.   positioned underneath the product container.
   e.   positioned in the channel underneath the product.

5.   List three types of convenience goods.

   a.
   b.
   c.

Check your responses on page 141.

III. CONTROLLABLE OTC MERCHANDISING FACTORS

This section will discuss those elements of merchandising display that are critical to the construction of a planogram. All of these elements are directly controllable by pharmacy management.

A. SHELF FACINGS

Careful allocation of shelf facings can benefit the community pharmacist by increasing the overall profitability. As mentioned earlier, shelf facings refer to the frontward and upright display of the primary selling surfaces of OTC products. Of course, the proper allocation of shelf facings requires planning, rearrangement, and constant management control. Optimum allocation of shelf facings increases profit through increased sales. Not only are individual product shelf facings necessary to promote increased sales, but the proper placement of product categories within the pharmacy induces sales increases.

The overall criterion for the proper allocation of shelf facings should be the correlation of shelf facings with national and regional sales; that is, the products which have the greatest sales within a category should have the maximum shelf facings. It has been demonstrated that increased shelf facings increase the visual contact of the product and, thus, gain attention. Once the customer's attention is gained, the packaging informs him of the product's characteristics, and potential sales are facilitated. Additionally, the sales of the nationally leading products appear to be the most sensitive to shelf facings. Part of the cause for this relationship is the fact that many over the-counter leaders receive substantial national advertising, and the increased shelf facings serve to remind the purchaser of the promotional message, and so the sale is consummated.

B. HORIZONTAL AND VERTICAL LOCATION OF PRODUCTS

It is a well-recognized fact that the products which sell the fastest are those located on a horizontal plane at the eye level of the average female customer (about five feet). The great majority of OTC pharmacy products are purchased by females. Even as much as 80% of men's shaving needs are purchased by females. Additionally, the products which sell best are located in a vertical line in the center of the product category display, thus giving rise to the term "hot-spot cross" (illustrated below). The fastest selling area within a given display is at the eye-level location, and the next best selling area is at the vertical axis at the center of the product category display.

THE
HOT-SPOT
CROSS

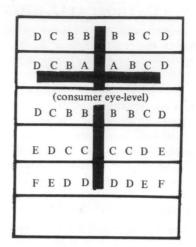

FIGURE 1. The Hot-Spot Cross Principle of positioning products in a department, in which "A" represents the best position, "B" the next best position, and so on. The fastest-moving products are normally assigned position "A".

Used with permission from Slater, R. E. "OTC Merchandising." In *Effective Pharmacy Management.* Kansas City, MO: Marion Laboratories, Inc., 1979.

The pharmacy owner/manager may also consider assigning a vertical arrangement to a product category, as opposed to the traditional horizontal arrangement. In a vertical arrangement, each product is displayed on a vertical axis with the largest size usually located at eye level. The vertical arrangement requires additional shelf space and added control, when compared to the horizontal arrangement scheme. For these reasons, the vertical arrangement has not been popular with many pharmacy owner/managers; however, for special promotions and displays at the end of merchandise gondolas (end-cap displays), the vertical display has proven effective.

C. PLACEMENT OF PRODUCT SIZES

Sales volume, in dollars, tends to increase when the largest size of a product is located to the right of the smaller size of the same product. The "right-hand rule" of merchandising is based upon the fact that most people are right-handed and will tend to select products from the right. Also, people read from left to right and will tend to remember the last size viewed.

D. LOCATION OF PRODUCT SECTIONS

Location of a product category within the pharmacy is an important management decision. Most people will turn to their right and proceed to the back of the pharmacy upon entering a community pharmacy. Thus, the greatest unit sales are possible on the displays in the right, front portion of the pharmacy.

Generally speaking, the remaining front portions of the pharmacy afford good potential for sales because of increased foot traffic. Sales potential diminishes as one proceeds to the rear of the drug store. By sales potential, we mean those incremental sales gained from good merchandising techniques and/or implementation of planograms.

Let us consider the location of an emergency first-aid department and an analgesic-sedative department within the pharmacy. The placement of the fast-moving analgesic department in a high-traffic area will increase profit to a greater degree than would the same placement of the slower-moving emergency first-aid department. It is true that slower-moving departments will increase their sales when placed in high-traffic areas in the front portions of the pharmacy; however, since the initial base sales of the slower-moving department are low, the optimum strategy is to expose the high-volume departments to the maximum traffic flow in order to maximize overall store sales.

E. LOCATION OF THE PHARMACY DEPARTMENT

The pharmacy department is usually located at the rear of the drug store. In order to have a prescription filled, the patient must pass a large number of displays. The maximum exposure to displays is an important consideration when one considers that as many as 40% of the nonprescription purchases are unplanned before entering the community pharmacy.

IV. IMPLEMENTING PLANOGRAMS

The interpretation of planograms is an art. Planograms are constructed on the premise that sales can be increased by increasing the allocations of shelf facings and placement of the national and regional sales leaders. As we have learned, many other factors affect the responsiveness of sales to merchandising display. It is the owner/manager's responsibility to assimilate the trends in arriving at a decision.

Many successful OTC pharmacy owner/managers have implemented planograms. From their experiences, we can draw several general and specific conclusions.

A. CLERK INTERVENTION

Clerks must not be allowed to determine the allocation of shelf facings and product placement. The common tendency is to reduce the shelf facings of the leading products when their stocks are temporarily low. In doing so, the clerks will expand the shelf facings of the competing products whose sales are not as great as those of the leading products. The net effect is that the overall sales of the department are reduced because of the improper allocation of shelf facings.

B. BREADTH OF ASSORTMENT

Adoption of a planogram calls for the maximization of the leading national or regional brands. Situations may arise where the overall breadth of the product section is severely curtailed. Pharmacy OTC merchandising, as compared to mass merchandising, offers a full assortment of OTC merchandise. If shelf space is limited, the best strategy is to reduce to a minimum the shelf facings of the slower-moving items.

C. STAGNATION OF SALES

A pharmacy owner/manager may implement a planogram for most of the sections of the OTC merchandise. He may find, however, that a particular department does not increase its sales despite implementation of the planogram. The best strategy in such a situation is change. Many times dramatic sales are seen in a department which is moved from one section of a pharmacy to another that receives greater customer traffic. At the very minimum, the shelf facings and shelf placement of the entire department should be changed.

Planograms do work; however, they are based upon national and regional sales figures. If local conditions do not reflect the national trends, the planogram will not increase the sales volume. In this case, it is best to experiment by increasing the shelf facings of those products the owner/manager believes to be the leaders in the local area.

D. SEASONAL MERCHANDISE

Planograms reflect past sales trends. In fact, they may be several weeks or months behind the current trends. Seasonal merchandise may not be reflected in planograms. In this case, the pharmacy owner/manager should anticipate seasonal sales and be willing to digress from the planogram.

E. FREE DISPLAY MATERIALS

Many times clerks will discard free display materials such as product spotters. These display materials are highly effective in stimulating individual product sales. Discarding such materials is a waste of free sales promotion. On the other hand, most display cartons require additional shelf facings. In this situation, it is best to discard those display cartons which do not match the shelf facings assigned by the planogram.

The successful OTC merchandiser is not willing to accept stagnation of sales, but instead is eager to experiment continually in order to improve his sales and profit position.

REVIEW QUESTIONS (III & IV)

DIRECTIONS: Circle the appropriate letter or supply the information requested in each of the following.

T   F   1.   The overall criterion for the proper allocation of shelf facings should be the correlation of shelf facings with national and regional sales.

T   F   2.   The great majority of OTC products is purchased by male customers.

T   F   3.   Clerks can be depended upon to maintain a planogram once established.

T   F   4.   Planograms do a good job of predicting national sales trends but only a fair job of predicting local sales trends.

T   F   5.   Seasonal sales trends are reflected in planograms.

T   F   6.   Display cartons should be used even if they exceed the shelf facings assigned by the planogram.

7.   List five factors of OTC merchandising display which are essential for the construction of a planogram.

 a.

 b.

 c.

 d.

 e.

Check your responses on page 141.

ANSWERS TO REVIEW QUESTIONS

I & II
1. T
2. F
3. T
4. c,d
5. In any order:
   a. staple goods
   b. impulse goods
   c. emergency goods

III & IV
1. T
2. F
3. F
4. T
5. F
6. F
7. In any order:
   a. shelf facings
   b. horizontal and vertical product location
   c. placement of product sizes
   d. location of product sections
   e. location of the pharmacy department

RECOMMENDED FOLLOW-UP

For further information concerning pharmacy management and OTC merchandising, it is recommended that the user study the following reference:

Slater, R. E. "OTC Merchandising." In *Effective Pharmacy Management.* Kansas City, MO: Marion Laboratories, Inc., 1979, pp. 309-329.

APPENDIX 1

ANALGESIC, SEDATIVE HIGHLIGHTS

Market Share	Drug	44%	**Department Size**	8'
	Food	48%		
	MM	8%	**Recommended No.**	
			of Linear Feet	72'
Drug Sales Index	80%			
			Estimated Sales	
Estimated Gross Margin	24%		**per Month**	$900-$1700

IMPORTANCE

Although the supermarkets own the largest share of this giant $1.2 billion market, the drug trade's 44% share means that over $500 million is spent on Analgesics in drugstores annually.

DEPARTMENT MAKEUP

Internal Analgesics, Sedatives	**80%**
Extra-strength Pain Relievers	32%
Regular Strength Pain Relievers	26%
Child	7%
Arthritis/Rheumatism	5%
Menstrual	3%
Sedatives/Stimulants	5%
Motion Sickness	2%
External Analgesics	**20%**
Pain Relieving Rubs/Ointments	9%
Liniments/Liquids	3%
Hemorrhoidals	8%

Extra-strength and capsule have been the key words describing changes within the internal analgesic section. The 1981 plan-o-gram contains 8 new capsule SKU's: 4 regular strength and 4 extra-strength; plus 2 new extra-strength tablets.

The five leading brands: Tylenol, Anacin, Bayer, Excedrin, and Bufferin dominate the internal analgesic segment with a combined market share of about 65% in drugstores. Drugstore brands such as Ascriptin, Empirin, Percogesic and Ecotrin together command an additional 14%.

HOW TO BUILD BUSINESS

1. Adjust assortment to include new products and to reflect gains made by Tylenol.
2. Promote the best size of the best brands often; extra-strength Tylenol capsules 50's and tablets 60's; Tylenol, Anacin, Bayer, Excedrin and Bufferin 100's.
3. Give good shelf location to drugstore brands Ascriptin, Empirin, Percogesic and Ecotrin. Remind staff to recommend them.
4. Stock and suggest generic aspirin 100's, 250's and Children's 36's. Use generic APAP 100's if they are available and offer good profit plus customer savings.
5. Tie-in extra sales such as fever thermometers in Analgesic section.

GROWTH POTENTIAL

The department grew about 16% last year. Although a large portion of the gain can be attributed to inflation, a real growth of about 4% on a huge $1 billion+ base is very encouraging. Extra-strength products are the fastest growing area.

Aspercreme grew well in the external analgesics and advertising on the new hemorrhoidals may boost that flat category next year.

BEST SELLERS

Internal Analgesics
Tylenol Extra-strength Capsules 50's
Anacin 100's
Bayer 100's
Bufferin 100's
Tylenol 100's
Tylenol Extra-strength Tablets 60's
Excedrin 100's

Sedatives/Stimulants
Unisom 16's
Sominex 32's
Vivarin 40's
No Doz 15's

Pain Relief Rubs
Ben Gay Greaseless 1.25 oz
Aspercreme 3 oz

Hemorrhoidals
Prep H Suppositories 12's, 24's
Prep H Ointment 1 oz
Lanacane 1 oz

MERCHANDISING NOTES

1. Include Analgesics in your winter Cough & Cold displays.
2. Display Anacin and Bayer tins near pharmacy cash register.
3. Include children's pain relievers in baby section as well as in analgesic section. Advertise in multiples.
4. Selectively buy and display floorstands or counter units of best selling analgesics, especially on dating deals in Fall and Winter.
5. Use "compare and save" signs if you have good generic aspirin.

PRICING STRATEGY

You must be **very** competitive on best selling sizes of top internal analgesics. Be sure your smaller sizes are priced lower than best selling size. Bufferin 60's priced the same or more than Bufferin 100's, for example, leaves a tacky impression with the consumer.

Large sizes have consumer appeal if the per tablet price is less than that of best selling size. Large size generic aspirin is especially popular as is large size Anacin. Monitor your stock of large sizes very carefully, however, as they can take a large bite out of your inventory budget. Shop your best supermarket competitor on AAA items and **meet** his price. Shop your best drug competitor on selected AA items and price your AA s slightly higher. A items need little or no discount.

ANALGESICS, SEDATIVES
(No. 157; Model A, B, C; 8 Ft. Wall; 86'' High)

SHELF #1 (Bottom)	Facing	SHELF #2	Facing
Tucks 12's	1	Tucks Ointment 40 gr.	1
Tucks 40's	1	Vaseline Hemor-Aid 2 oz	1
Tucks 100's	1	Medicone Suppositories 12's	1
Dermoplast 3 oz	1	Pazo Suppositories 12's	1
Balneol 4 oz	1	Pazo Ointment 1 oz	1
Peterson's Ointment 1.4 oz	1	Pazo Ointment 2 oz	1
Peterson's Ointment 3.0 oz	1	Wyanoids Supp 12's	1
Regional Space		Diothane Ointment 1 oz	1
Ben Gay Lotion 2 oz	1	Medicone Ointment 1.5 oz	1
Ben Gay Lotion 4 oz	1	Xylocaine 2.5 oz	1
Deep Heating 2 oz	1	Amercaine 1 oz	1
Deep Heating 4 oz	1	Nupercainal Suppositories 12's	1
Banalg 2 oz	1	Nupercainal Ointment 1 oz	1
Emul-o-Balm 4 oz	1	Nupercainal Ointment 2 oz	1
Mobisyl 3.5 oz	1	*Regional Space*	
Heet 2.5 oz	1	Dermolate	1
Heet 5.0 oz	1	Cortef Ointment ½ oz	1
Absorbine 4 oz	1	Cortaid Ointment ½ oz	1
Aborbine Jr. 12 oz	1	Lanacane 1 oz	1
Sloan's Ointment 7 oz	1	Lanacane 2.5 oz	1
Omega 4.85 oz	1	Deep Heating Ointment 1.3 oz	1
Purepac Rubbing Alcohol 16 oz	1	Deep Heating Ointment 3.3 oz	1
Lavacol 16 oz	1	Musterole 1 oz	1
Crystal Alcohol 16 oz 70%	1	Infra-Rub 1.3 oz	1
Crystal Alcohol 16 oz 91%	1	Infra-Rub 3.3 oz	1
		Regional Space	
		Minit-Rub 1.5 oz	1
		Minit-Rub 3.0 oz	1
		Myoflex Creme 2 oz	1

SHELF #3	Facing
Tronolane Suppositories 10's	1
Tronolane Ointment 1 oz	1
Tronolane Ointment 2 oz	1
Anusol Suppositories 12's	1
Anusol Suppositories 24's	1
Anusol Ointment 1 oz	1
Preparation H 12's	1
Preparation H 24's	1
Preparation H 48's	1
Preparation H 1 oz	1
Preparation H 2 oz	1
Saratoga Ointment 1 oz	1
Saratoga Ointment 2 oz	1
Ben Gay Gel 1.25 oz	1
Ben Gay Gel 3.0 oz	1
Ben Gay Original 1.25 oz	1
Ben Gay Original 3.0 oz	1
Ben Gay Extra Strength Balm 3.75 oz	1
Icy Hot 1.25 oz	1
Icy Hot 3.5 oz	1
Icy Hot 7.0 oz	1
Deep-Down 1.25 oz	1
Deep-Down 3.0 oz	1

SHELF #4	Facing
Bayer Arthritis Aspirin 72's	1
Bayer Arthritis Aspirin 125's	1
Anacin Arthritis Formula 40's	1
Anacin Arthritis Formula 100's	1

SHELF #4 (continued)	Facing
Anacin Arthritis Formula 175's	1
Bufferin Arthritis Strength 40's	1
Bufferin Arthritis Strength 100's	1
Ecotrin 100's	1
Ecotrin 250's	1
Ascriptin A/D 100's	2
Ascriptin A/D 500's	2
Ben Gay Greaseless 1.25 oz	1
Ben Gay Greaseless 3.0 oz	1
Ben Gay Greaseless 5.0 oz	1
Aspercreme 1.25 oz	1
Aspercreme 3.0 oz	1
Aspercreme 5.0 oz	1
Aspercreme 6.0 oz	1

SHELF #5	Facing
Momentum 24's	1
Momentum 48's	1
Doans Pills 24's	1
Doans Pills 48's	1
Cystex 24's	1
Liquiprin 1.15 oz	1
Tempra ½ oz	1
Aspirin-Free Tempra 4 oz	1
St. Joseph Child's Aspirin 36's	1
Bayer Child's Aspirin 36's	1
Tylenol Chewable Tablets 30's	1
Tylenol Elixir 2 oz	1
Tylenol Elixir 4 oz	1

SHELF #5 (continued)

	Facing
Tylenol Drops ½ oz	1
Ascriptin 50's	1
Ascriptin 100's	2
Ascriptin 500's	2
Empirin 50's	2
Empirin 100's	2
Empirin 250's	1
Cama Tablets 100's	1
Purepac Aspirin 100's	1
Purepac Aspirin 100's	2
Norwich 250's	1
Norwich 500's	1

SHELF #6

	Facing
Bayer 12's	1
Bayer 24's	1
Bayer 50's	1
Bayer 100's	3
Byaer 200's	1
Bayer 300's	1
Tylenol Reg. Strength 24's	1
Tylenol Reg. Strength 100's	3
Tylenol Reg. Strength 200's	2
Tylenol Reg. Strength Caps 24's	1
Tylenol Reg. Strength Caps 50's	1
Tylenol Reg. Strength Caps 100's	1
Bufferin 12's	1
Bufferin 36's	1
Bufferin 60's	1

SHELF #6 (continued)

	Facing
Bufferin 100's	2
Bufferin 165's	1
Bufferin 375's	1
Bufferin Ex-Strength 50's	1
Bufferin Ex-Strength Caps 24's	1
Bufferin Ex-Strength Caps 50's	1

SHELF #7

	Facing
Excedrin 12's	1
Excedrin 36's	1
Excedrin 60's	1
Excedrin 100's	2
Excedrin 225's	1
Excedrin Ex-Strength Caps 40's	1
Excedrin Ex-Strength Caps 60's	1
Tylenol Liquid 8 oz	1
Tylenol Ex-Strength 24's	1
Tylenol Ex-Strength 50's	2
Tylenol Ex-Strength 100's	1
Tylenol Ex-Strength Caps 24's	1
Tylenol Ex-Strength Caps 50's	2
Tylenol Ex-Strength Caps 100's	2
Anacin 12's	1
Anacin 30's	1
Anacin 50's	1
Anacin 100's	3
Anacin 200's	1
Anacin 300's	1

144d

SHELF #8	Facing
Excedrin PM 30's	1
Excedrin PM 50's	1
Excedrin PM 80's	1
Unisom 8's	1
Unisom 16's	1
Sominex 16's	1
Sominex 32's	1
Sominex 72's	1
Sominex 124's	1
BC Pain Relief 6's	1
Regional Space	
Cope 36's	1
Percogesics 24's	1
Percogesics 100's	1
Vanquish 60's	1
Vanquish 100's	1
Datril 100's	1
Datril 500 72's	1
Gemnisyn 100's	1
Lilly A.S.A. Tablets 100's	1
Anacin–3 30's	1
Anacin–3 60's	1
Anacin Maximum Strength 20's	1
Anacin Maximum Strength 40's	1
Anacin Maximum Strength 75's	1
Anacin Maximum Strength Caps 36's	1

Reprinted through the courtesy of
Hamacher and Associates, Inc.
Wauwatosa, Wisconsin

SHELF #9	Facing
Quiet World 12's	1
Nytol 16's	1
Nytol 32's	1
Nytol 72's	1
Sleep-Eze 10's	1
Compoz 12's	1
Nervine 30's	1
Regional Space	
Dramamine 12's	1
Dramamine 36's	1
Dramamine Jr. 3 Oz	
Bonine 8's	1
Marezine 12's	1
Vivarin 16's	1
Vivarin 40's	1
Vivarin 80's	1
No-Doz 15's	1
No-Doz 36's	1
No-Doz 60's	1
Trendar 24's	1
Trendar 50's	1
Midol 12's	1
Midol 30's	1
Midol 60's	1
Pamprin 24's	1
Pamprin 48's	1
Aspergum Cherry 16's	1
Aspergum Orange 16's	1
Aspergum Orange 40's	1

APPENDIX 2

BERGEN BRUNSWIG DRUG COMPANY
SPACE MANAGER PROGRAM
PLAN-O-GRAM IMPLEMENTATION FORM

NATIONAL:

CODE # DESCRIPTION	## ## ## ## ## ## ## ## FACINGS ## ##							
	15	20	25	30	35	40	45	50

POSITION 1

CODE # DESCRIPTION	15	20	25	30	35	40	45	50
149-948 NEOSPORIN OINT 1/2OZ	1	1	1	1	2	2	2	2
149-963 NEOSPORIN OINT 1OZ	1	1	1	1	1	1	1	1
107-169 VASELINE JELLY 1 3/4OZ	1	1	1	1	1	1	1	1
107-201 VASELINE JELLY 3 3/4OZ	1	1	1	1	1	1	1	1
106-807 VAS CARBOLATED 1 3/4OZ	1	1	1	1	1	1	1	1
047-985 JJ FIRST AID CR 8OZ	1	1	1	1	1	1	1	1
048-009 JJ FIRST AID CR 1.5OZ	1	1	1	1	1	1	1	1
047-969 JJ FIRST AID CR 2.5OZ			1	1		1	1	1
215-806 SOLARCAINE CR 1OZ			1	1	1	1	1	1
215-814 SOLARCAINE CR 2OZ		1		1	1	1	1	1
216-002 SOLARCAINE LOT 3OZ			1	1	1	1	1	1
216-028 SOLARCAINE LOT 6OZ		1	1			1	1	1
216-036 SOL PUMP SP 3.5OZ			1	1	1	1	1	1
215-988 SOL AEROSOL 3OZ		1	1	1	1	1	1	1
216-283 SOL AEROSOL 5OZ		1		1	1	1	1	1
244-608 BACTINE SQUEEZE 2OZ	1	1	1	1	1	1	1	1
244-640 BACTINE SQUEEZE 4OZ		1	1	1	1	1	1	1
244-624 BACTINE SPRAY 3OZ		1	1	1	1	1	1	1
348-797 CAMPHO-GEL .23OZ	1	1	1	1	1	1	1	1
348-763 CAMPHO- 2OZ	1	1	1	1	1	1	1	1
348-789 CAMPHO- 4OZ	1	1	1	1	1	1	1	1
495-903 BFI POWDER 1 1/4OZ	1	1	1	1	1	1	1	1

BERGEN BRUNSWIG DRUG COMPANY
SPACE MANAGER PROGRAM
PLAN-O-GRAM IMPLEMENTATION FORM

NATIONAL:

POSITION 2

CODE #	DESCRIPTION	15	20	25	30	35	40	45	50
		‡ FACINGS ‡							
062-224	SPECTROCIN OINT 1/2OZ	1	1	1	1	1	1	2	2
062-240	SPECTROCIN OINT 1OZ	1	1	1	1	1	1	1	2
589-465	BETADINE OINT 1OZ	1	1	1	1	1	2	2	2
013-342	BACITRACIN OINT 1/2OZ	1	1	1	1	1	1	1	1
013-367	BACITRACIN OINT 1OZ	1	1	1	1	1	2	2	2
150-201	POLYSPORIN OINT 1/2OZ	1	1	1	1	1	2	2	2
150-227	POLYSPORIN OINT 1OZ	1	1	1	1	1	2	2	2
325-183	NEO-POLYCIN OINT 1/2OZ	1	1	1	1	1	1	2	2
325-191	NEO-POLYCIN OINT 1OZ	-	1	1	1	1	1	1	1
079-640	ACHROMYCIN OINT 1/2OZ	-	1	1	1	1	1	1	1
080-580	AUREOMYCIN OINT 1/2OZ	-	1	-	1	1	1	1	1
287-342	BACIQUENT OINT 1/2OZ	-	1	1	1	1	1	1	1
287-367	BACIQUENT OINT 1OZ	-	-	1	1	1	1	1	1
289-702	MYCIQUENT OINT 1/2OZ	-	-	1	1	1	1	1	1
289-728	MYCIQUENT OINT 1OZ	-	-	-	-	1	1	1	1
272-245	CLOVERINE SALVE 1OZ	-	-	-	1	1	1	1	1
323-246	BACIMYCIN OINT 1/2OZ	-	-	-	1	1	1	1	1
289-769	MYCITRACIN OINT 1/2OZ	1	1	1	1	1	1	2	2
628-149	NUMOTIZINE 4OZ	-	-	-	-	1	1	1	1
500-025	RESINOL OINT 1 1/4OZ	1	1	1	1	1	1	1	1
593-152	SAYMAN SALVE 1.5OZ	-	-	-	1	1	1	2	2
593-160	SAYMAN SALVE 4OZ	-	-	1	1	1	1	1	1
499-665	IODEX REG 1OZ	1	1	1	1	1	1	1	1
499-681	IODEX METHYL 1OZ	1	1	1	1	1	1	1	2

BERGEN BRUNSWIG DRUG COMPANY
SPACE MANAGER PROGRAM
PLAN-O-GRAM IMPLEMENTATION FORM

NATIONAL:

CODE # DESCRIPTION	\# \# \# \# \# \# FACINGS \# \# \# \# \#							
	15	20	25	30	35	40	45	50

POSITION 3

CODE # DESCRIPTION	15	20	25	30	35	40	45	50
408-765 UNGUENTINE BURNS 1OZ	1	1	1	1	1	1	1	1
408-443 UNGUENTINE + 1OZ	-	-	-	1	1	1	1	1
408-468 UNGUENTINE + 2OZ	-	-	-	-	1	1	1	1
408-427 UNGUENTINE SUNBRN 5OZ	1	1	1	1	1	1	1	1
492-694 KIP BURNS 1OZ	1	1	1	1	1	2	2	2
527-853 AMERICAINE OINT 3/4OZ	-	-	-	1	1	1	1	1
564-278 AMERICAINE SP 4OZ	-	-	-	-	1	1	1	1
448-639 MEDI-QUICK PUMP 4OZ	-	-	-	-	-	1	1	1
448-621 MEDI-QUICK SP 3OZ	1	1	1	1	1	1	1	1
048-504 J&J CLINICAINE SP 2OZ	-	-	-	1	1	1	1	1
048-512 J&J CLINICAINE PUMP SP	-	-	-	1	1	1	1	1
048-520 J&J CLINICYDIN OINT 1.5OZ	-	1	1	1	1	1	1	1
048-538 J&J CLINICYDIN OINT 1OZ	-	1	1	1	1	1	1	1
048-546 J&J CLINICORT CRE 1.5OZ	-	1	1	1	1	1	1	1
048-533 J&J CLINICORT CRE 1OZ	-	1	1	1	1	1	1	1
048-561 J&J CLINICORT PUMP SP 1.5OZ	1	1	1	1	1	1	1	1
590-729 FOILLE OINT TUBE 1OZ	1	1	1	1	1	1	1	1
590-745 FOILLE OINT SP 3 1/4OZ	1	1	1	1	1	1	1	1
299-388 DOMEBORO TAB 12S	1	1	1	1	1	1	2	2
299-321 DOMEBORO POW 12S	1	1	1	1	1	1	2	2
281-501 MERCUROCHROME 1OZ	1	1	1	1	1	2	2	2
029-801 MERTHIOLATE 3/4OZ	1	1	1	1	1	1	2	2
001-024 MERTHIOLATE AERO 6OZ	1	1	1	1	1	1	1	1

BERGEN BRUNSWIG DRUG COMPANY
SPACE MANAGER PROGRAM
PLAN-O-GRAM IMPLEMENTATION FORM

NATIONAL:

CODE # DESCRIPTION	15	20	25	30	35	40	45	50
	-------			---PLAN FOOTAGE---				-------
	#	#	#	# FACINGS #	#	#	#	#

POSITION 4

CODE # DESCRIPTION	15	20	25	30	35	40	45	50
330-423 CRUEX CR .530Z	1	1	2	2	2	2	2	2
330-308 CRUEX POWDER 1.50Z	1	2	2	2	2	2	2	2
330-316 CRUEX POWDER 30Z	1	1	2	2	2	2	2	2
330-324 CRUEX SPRAY POW 1.80Z	1	2	2	2	2	2	2	2
330-340 CRUEX SP POW 3 1/20Z	1	2	2	2	2	2	2	2
471-805 DERMOPLAST SP 30Z	1	2	2	2	2	2	2	2
471-821 DERMOPLAST SP 60Z	1	2	2	2	2	2	2	2
564-351 AMERICAINE AEROSOL 20Z	1	2	2	2	2	2	2	2
564-344 AMERICAINE AEROSOL 40Z	1	2	2	2	2	2	2	2
570-739 SEA BREEZE BREEZETTS 24S	1	1	1	1	1	1	1	1
570-689 SEA BREEZE 40Z	1	1	1	1	1	1	1	1
570-705 SEA BREEZE 100Z	1	1	1	1	2	2	2	2
570-721 SEA BREEZE 16OZ	1	1	1	1	1	2	2	2

BERGEN BRUNSWIG DRUG COMPANY
SPACE MANAGER PROGRAM
PLAN-O-GRAM IMPLEMENTATION FORM

NATIONAL:

CODE # DESCRIPTION				PLAN FOOTAGE				
	15	20	25	30	35	40	45	50
FACINGS	#	#	#	#	#	#	#	#
POSITION 5								
899-476 AFTER BITE 14CC	-	1	1	1	1	2	2	2
500-413 STING KILL SWABS 5EA	-	1	1	1	1	2	2	2
433-409 RANTEX WIPE 14S	-	1	1	1	1	2	2	2
433-417 RANTEX WIPE 36S	1	1	1	1	1	2	2	2
186-262 PREP H PAD 40S	1	1	1	1	1	2	2	2
186-270 PREP H PAD 100S	1	1	1	1	1	2	2	2
500-983 TUCKS PAD 12S	1	1	1	1	1	2	2	2
500-884 TUCKS PAD 40S	1	1	1	1	1	2	2	2
500-900 TUCKS PAD 100S	1	-	1	1	1	2	2	2
500-769 ARD PAD 24S	-	-	1	1	1	1	1	2
074-625 LAVACOL 16OZ	-	-	-	-	-	1	3	3

POST-TEST

NOTE TO CONTINUING EDUCATION USERS

To obtain CE credit, remove the appropriate sheet from the accompanying answer sheet booklet and follow the directions for completing the post-test and applying for credit.

DIRECTIONS: Indicate which of the following statements are true (T) and which are false (F) by circling the appropriate letter.

T F 1. The Bergen Brunswig planogram allows the pharmacy owner/manager to expand or contract individual departments easily.

T F 2. Generally speaking, product sales are most responsive to shelf facings at the maturity stage of the product life cycle.

T F 3. Products of a single category which are intensely competitive should be allowed minimum shelf space.

T F 4. A channel strip calls attention to a particular product, but has not proven to be effective in increasing sales.

T F 5. The Bergen Brunswig planogram allows for department sizes between 15 and 50 feet and is, therefore, more flexible than the Associated Druggist planogram.

DIRECTIONS: Circle the letter corresponding to the **one** correct answer in each of the following.

6. A given product will sell best when located

   a. at eye level for the average man.
   b. at the right-most side of the department.
   c. in the stock room.
   d. in the center of the product category display.
   e. at the left-most side of the department.

7. Products located on a shelf that is about five feet high

   a. will sell better than products located at the other heights.
   b. are most difficult to control.
   c. are most easily spotted by the average female customer.
   d. b and c only.
   e. a and c only.

8. An OTC merchandise display which places different sizes of products in a vertical line

   a. is not an effective promotional display.
   b. is effective as an end-cap display.
   c. requires less shelf space than does a horizontal display.
   d. requires equal shelf space when compared to a horizontal display.

9. Larger sizes of the same product are located to the right of the smaller sizes because

    a.   most people are right-handed and tend to reach for an item with the right hand.

    b.   people read from left to right and will tend to remember the last size viewed.

    c.   sales volume tends to increase with this strategy.

    d.   all of the above.

    e.   a and c only.

10. Impulse goods

    a.   should receive maximum shelf facings.
    b.   are purchased after consideration of costs and quality.
    c.   should be placed in the front portion of the pharmacy.
    d.   require little planning on the part of the pharmacy owner/manager.
    e.   a and c only.

11. Staple items are

    a.   purchased on an urgent basis.

    b.   usually purchased with thorough planning.

    c.   classified by considering the general product category in the mind of the typical customer.

    d.   not at all responsive to shelf facings.

    e.   purchased routinely without much thought.

12. Rank the following categories of convenience goods (from **lowest** to **highest**) in terms of the relative importance of their shelf facings on sales responsiveness: A=Staple goods; B=Emergency goods; C=Impulse goods.

    a.   C, A, B
    b.   C, B, A
    c.   B, C, A
    d.   B, A, C

13. For the effective management of planograms,

    a.   clerks should not be permitted to determine shelf facings.
    b.   seasonal merchandise should be anticipated.
    c.   free display materials should not be used.
    d.   all of the above.
    e.   a and b only.

NOTE TO OTHER USERS

The answers to the post-test are provided in the accompanying answer booklet for users who do not wish to obtain continuing education credit.

Unit Seven

Advertising Media
Selection and Costs

Robert N. Zelnio, Ph.D.
College of Pharmacy
University of Iowa

TABLE OF CONTENTS

Study Time: **1.5 hours**
CE Credit: **.15 CEU**

INTRODUCTION

The selection of a medium is only one of the considerations in the planning of an advertising campaign. The diversity of advertising media, the proportion of costs attributable to a medium, and the necessity of proper placement for the successful use of advertising all add to the importance of this facet of advertising.

The purpose of this unit, therefore, is to discuss aspects of media selection, characteristics of media that are relevant to the selection decision, and the costs associated with advertising media.

OBJECTIVES

The objectives are presented here to aid the user in focusing attention on expected learning outcomes.

Upon completion of this unit, the user should be able to:

1. Distinguish between retail and other forms of advertising.

2. Distinguish between the different objectives attained through advertising.

3. Recognize examples of the types of advertising media.

4. Distinguish between media and media vehicles.

5. Recall the characteristics of individual advertising media.

6. Perform audience measurement computations for various media.

7. Calculate the comparative cost of a media vehicle.

RECOMMENDED PREPARATION

This unit is intended for use by pharmacy students, practicing pharmacists, and pharmacy owner/managers. In order to derive the maximum benefit from this unit, the following references on marketing, promotion, and aspects of advertising other than those discussed here are recommended reading prior to beginning this unit.

Gagnon, J. P. *Managing the Advertising Expense in a Community Pharmacy.* Vol. IV, No. 2 of *The Pharmacist's Business Notebook.* New York: Biomedical Information Corporation, 1980, pp. 3-11.

Smith, H. A. "Promotion." In *Principles and Methods of Pharmacy Management.* 2nd ed. Philadelphia: Lea and Febiger, 1980, pp. 286-306.

Zelnio, R. N. "Planning for Pharmacy Marketing." *Pharmacy Management,* 151(4): 164-169, 173, 1979.

I. PRINCIPLES OF RETAIL ADVERTISING

Advertising was defined by the American Marketing Association as a paid form of nonpersonal presentation and promotion of ideas, goods, or services by an identified sponsor. While this definition applies to all advertisers, pharmacists, as retailers, are concerned with advertising that is different in many respects from that done by manufacturers, wholesalers, or other members of the distribution channel.

First, retail advertising is both large and small in scope. It is large in that the retailer is involved with all aspects of preparing the ad, buying time or space, and the technical production details. Larger advertisers typically retain advertising agencies to perform such tasks. From a different perspective, retail advertising is small in scope because it is aimed at smaller, local populations rather than national audiences.

A second difference is that retail ads operate at only one level of the channel of distribution in seeking to influence the behavior or attitudes of consumers. Other forms of advertising may operate at any of three levels, by seeking to influence consumers, other channel members, or dealer effectiveness.

The content of retail advertisements also serves to differentiate retail ads from the ads of manufacturers and other organizations. Because retailers have a better knowledge of local market conditions, they advertise products from the view that consumers should purchase them from specific sources, and often advertise prices, styles, sizes, types, or brands of products as factors that support this view. National advertisers, on the other hand, cannot use such factors in their ads because they are not aware of the prices at which products sell or the styles, sizes, types, or brands that are popular in local markets.

Another aspect of advertising content is appeal. Retail ads tend to be factual and rational in their attempts to influence consumers, while other advertisers are more likely to use emotional and imaginative appeals.

Finally, retail advertisers use newspapers to a greater extent and television to a lesser extent than do other advertisers.

While these distinctions influence all aspects of retail advertising, advertising objectives warrant special attention. Such objectives not only influence media selection, but also set the standards against which these and other decisions are judged.

A. ADVERTISING OBJECTIVES

Although all business activities should ultimately lead to increased profits, two types of advertising objectives contribute specifically to this responsibility.

1. *Target Objectives.* These objectives specify the audience that is to be reached with the message. The target market is a portion of the total market—defined by geographic, demographic, or product-usage characteristics—that is of primary interest to the advertiser. Thus, target objectives typically

specify a percent of the target market that is to be reached with the advertisement.

For example, a pharmacy owner/manager might specify a target market composed of all women between the ages of 18 and 35 and everyone over 55 living within a 3-mile radius of his pharmacy. This target would include individuals expected to have high demand for prescription and OTC drug products, i.e., women in the child-bearing ages and the elderly, who could conveniently patronize the pharmacy. The target objective would be specified as a percent of this population for whom content objectives are realized.

2. *Content Objectives.* These objectives specify the outcome which the advertiser wishes to accomplish in the target market. The advertiser may want to increase consumer awareness of, or interest in, the pharmacy's products or services or may wish to motivate consumers to evaluate, try, or adopt such products and services.

As an example, consider the pharmacy with the target market specified above. Suppose the owner/manager institutes a new hypertension screening service. A logical combination of target and content objectives might be to make 75% of the target market aware of the service and to make 25% try it during the first two weeks.

This objective will then dictate the type of media and media vehicles the pharmacy retailer should use and the ways they are used. The medium's audience must be matched with the target market, and the message used to accomplish content objectives must be consistent with the medium's capabilities.

B. ADVERTISING MEDIA

The media available for use in achieving both target and content objectives can be classified into five types. Broadcast media include television and radio. Print media include newspapers, magazines, the yellow pages, and shoppers' guides. Signs, billboards, and transit advertising are components of outdoor advertising. A fourth type of advertising comes under the heading of direct mail. And, lastly, in-store advertising includes the pharmacy's windows, displays, and point-of-purchase materials. Each of these media can be subdivided into media vehicles.

While an advertising medium is a communication channel through which a message is delivered, media vehicles are the modes of delivery. Vehicles are specific examples of each type of media. For example, television vehicles include specific programs such as the daytime dramas, nightly news, televised sports, and others. Radio stations adopt different formats and also have a variety of programs that constitute their vehicles. Newspaper vehicles include nationally known editions such as the *Wall Street Journal* or the *Washington Post,* as well as a myriad of local papers. Thus, each medium has its own vehicles.

Each vehicle attracts audiences of different sizes, compositions, and locations. In addition, each vehicle has its own advantages, and the task of media selection is made difficult for pharmacy retailers who cannot afford to retain advertising agencies. Nevertheless, there are some common aspects to the strategy of media selection.

C. MEDIA SELECTION STRATEGY

The successful media strategy normally calls for the use of a medium or combination of media in such a way that coverage, impact, and frequency are in balance. From the pharmacy advertisers's point of view, a fourth factor, administration, is important. Each of these factors is dependent upon a subset of media characteristics as discussed below.

1. *Coverage.*   In general, coverage is concerned with the people to whom the message is delivered. The strategy is to coordinate the circulation, or audience, of the medium with the characteristics of the pharmacy's target market. The characteristics most commonly used are geographic, demographic, or product use.

a. *Reach.*   The quantitative dimension of coverage, reach, is defined as the number of people to whom the message is delivered. To attract new customers, one strategy is to use media which cover the market by an amount slightly larger than the pharmacy's trading area. The challenge, however, is to avoid excess coverage to the point that the pharmacy's advertising funds are wasted.

The cumulative reach or "cume" is the building of an advertisement's audience over time. In other words, cume is the sum of all people reached by an ad during the period of its use. The cume is more than the one-time reach of an advertisement, but less than the theoretical coverage, because some of the people in the audience will never see the ad. The cume becomes larger as the length of time an advertisement runs and the frequency of its appearance are increased.

Audience duplication is a relevant concern when more than one medium is used. Duplication is the overlapping of the audiences of two or more media vehicles. If duplication occurs, coverage is not increased, but frequency does increase.

b. *Selectivity.*   The second dimension of coverage is selectivity. Selectivity is concerned with the quality of coverage, in that it refers to the ability of the medium to reach the desired target market efficiently. This dimension is sometimes called *effective reach* because the advertisement is most effective when it reaches the target market. While reach was achieved by matching the geographic location of the medium's audience with that of the pharmacy's trading area, selectivity involves matching the audience's demographic or product-use characteristics with those of the pharmacy's patrons.

2. *Impact.*   The second factor to be balanced in the media selection strategy is impact, or the extent to which the audience is influenced by the advertising. The impact a medium is capable of delivering is a function of many variables.

a. *Quality of reproduction.*   One such variable is the quality of reproduction. The better the creativity and technical production, the more likely the advertisement is to attract and hold an audience long enough to deliver the message. As a result, it is important to consider the facilities and capabilities a given media vehicle can offer to its clients. Although most, if not all, vehicles have some production and creative personnel that can assist in the design of ads, the nature of the medium may limit its ability to achieve high-quality reproduction. For example, newspapers can only reproduce color at high cost and under special conditions. Furthermore, the nature of the stock used in printing newspapers is such that photographs cannot be reproduced with high quality.

b. *Length of life.* The amount of time an advertisement is before an audience is called *length of life.* The longer the life of an ad, the greater its potential impact. Not only do more people see the ad, but they also have a longer period of time to grasp the message. Length of life is limited by the medium's capabilities. For instance, broadcast media are incapable of providing advertisements with long lives, due to the lack of a permanent record which remains after the ad has been aired. The print media, however, create such a record and, as a result, impart longer lives to their advertisements.

c. *Audience acceptance.* The impact a medium can have is also affected by its audience acceptance. Audience acceptance is generally high for an advertisement appearing in newspapers, magazines, and television and low for outdoor and direct mail advertising. The acceptance of the last two media is so low, in fact, that intended audience members often react negatively and may even actively avoid advertisements in these media.

d. *Clutter.* This variable refers to the competition an advertisement faces for the audience's attention and tends to reduce impact. Clutter can be measured by the number of ads running concurrently in a medium. It is also important to consider the contents of the competing ads and the medium's ability to allow the audience to receive them. For example, broadcast media are troubled by clutter because many commercials are aired in short time periods. However, television stations make an effort to avoid running advertisements for competing products in adjacent spots in an effort to minimize the harmful effects of clutter. Similarly, newspapers tend to be cluttered when the grocery ads appear and are always cluttered in the want-ad sections. However, because readers have the opportunity to study advertisements, if desired, clutter in newspapers is not felt to be a problem.

e. *Multi-channel capabilities.* One reason for television's superior impact is its ability to use more than one channel of communication, i.e., sight and sound. Thus, multi-channel capabilities, or the more senses a medium is able to employ in communicating with audiences, significantly improve impact. While television remains the leader in this area, recent advances, such as phonograph records flexible enough to be included in magazines and sent through the mail and "scratch and sniff" patches, have increased the channel capabilities of other media. Although they are not senses *per se,* television's ability to use motion and color probably contribute to its dominant impact.

f. *Flexibility.* The last variable to influence impact is flexibility. Flexibility is a function of the medium's leadtime, timeliness, and variety of acceptable formats. Leadtime is the amount of time between the deadline when the medium requires the advertisment to be submitted and the date when it is scheduled to run. The longer the leadtime, the farther ahead the advertisement must be submitted before its running date, and the less flexibility an advertiser has to change the copy to take advantage of current market trends. Timeliness refers to the medium's ability to deliver the message at desired times, e.g., to coincide with changes in the weather, the seasons, holidays, or market trends. A flexible medium is also capable of accepting and reproducing advertisements in varied formats. Magazines are generally inflexible due to the long leadtimes required, rigid and infrequent publication dates, and the limited number of formats which are acceptable. While radio and newspapers are generally flexible, they lose their flexibility where message formats are concerned.

3. *Frequency.* Frequency represents the number of times the message is delivered within a specified period. The importance of frequency is related to the fact that repeated exposures are required before a message is impressed upon the memories of a large proportion of the target market. Also, the message will be remembered longer as frequency increases. Some vehicles permit more frequency than others. Daily newspapers allow more frequency than weeklies, and those dailies with Sunday and holiday editions can deliver even greater frequency.

Continuity is related to frequency in that it is concerned with the length of time an advertising schedule runs without interruption. Good media planning calls for maintaining continuity with one medium, called the primary medium, and using a secondary medium when there is a need to increase frequency during special periods. The challenge is to use two media that can act synergistically. If the advertising budget is spread too thin, however, a problem may arise when funds are needed for special purposes later in the year.

Two other considerations related to frequency are seasonal programs and pulsation. Advertising should begin ahead of consumer-buying seasons and should appear in greater frequency so that consumers become aware of the approaching season and the pharmacy's product offerings. Pulsation is the use of several short bursts of advertising throughout the year in an effort to maintain awareness.

4. *Administration.* The administration of advertising media is of concern to pharmacy retailers because they cannot afford to retain professional advertising agencies to manage their campaigns. As a result, the more easily a medium can be managed, the less likely large amounts of pharmacy resources will be required to be spent on advertising.

a. *Costs.* Although a great deal more will be said about costs later in this unit, it is appropriate to note that two costs are of interest to advertisers. Total costs of producing and running an advertisement are important due to the pharmacy's budget limitations. However, cost per exposure, in one form or another, is relevant as a measure of the efficiency of advertising media. A rule of thumb is those media which minimize cost per exposure tend to be higher in total costs.

b. *Availability.* Availability of time or space is another administrative concern. The demands of coverage, impact, and frequency require that pharmacy advertisers have the ability to acquire specific amounts of time and space in selected media vehicles. The quantities required can be expected to vary with the time of the year, advertising objectives, length and complexity of messages, and other considerations. Furthermore, a great many variables beyond the control of advertisers influence the availability of time and space. For instance, the elections, special sporting events, number of media vehicles in an area, increases in postage rates, and legislation such as the Highway Beautification Act influence the availability of various media.

c. *Ease of purchase.* Ease of purchase is concerned with the difficulty advertisers have in contacting media vehicles needed to achieve advertising objectives. As the number of media vehicles increases, the ease of purchase decreases. This is particularly important to national advertisers or, perhaps, pharmacy chains seeking to advertise over larger geographic areas. For most pharmacy advertisers, however, the number of media vehicles to be used is small, and ease of purchase is not a significant problem.

d. *Flexibility.* Flexibility does not only influence the impact an advertisement may achieve, but also influences the administration of media. If a medium is particularly inflexible, pharmacy advertisers will be met with rigid leadtimes, timing and frequency opportunities, and ad-format requirements. Such lack of flexibility demands increased planning and, hence, a larger share of managerial resources. With the exception of frequency and continuity, which are highly dependent on the advertiser's strategy, the variables which should be considered when evaluating and selecting media are summarized in Table 1. In addition, each of the major media used by pharmacy retailers is rated on these variables. More often than not, however, pharmacy retailers are most severely limited by media costs. The remainder of this unit is devoted to the discussion of media costs and comparative cost calculations.

As stated earlier, the strategy behind the selection of advertising media requires that coverage, impact, frequency, and administration are all in balance and contribute to the attainment of advertising objectives.

Chain pharmacy organizations are able to use a wider range of media. National media such as television and magazines can be used to reach wider geographic and demographic markets. While the amount of reach and selectivity is greater than that needed by any single pharmacy, the excess will benefit other units in the chain. The chain can also advertise in local media, i.e., newspapers, radio, shoppers' guides, direct mail, or outdoor advertising to the benefit of individual pharmacies. Additionally, the use of such a wide variety of media will allow the chain to benefit from the superior impact of television, the local impact of newspapers and radio, as well as the frequency and administrative advantages of these and other media.

TABLE 1. Comparative Evaluation of Advertising Media

Media Characteristics	Television	Radio	Newspapers	Magazines	Shoppers' Guides
Reach	Very Good	Poor	Fair	Fair	Fair
Selectivity	Poor	Good Demographically	Good Geographically	Very Good	Poor
Quality of Reproduction	Varies with Reception	Fair	Poor	Very Good	Poor
Length of Life	Short	Short	Moderate	Long	Poor
Audience Acceptance	Good	Fair	Very Good	Good	Good
Clutter	High	Very High	High, but not a Problem	Moderate	Very High
Multi-Channel Capabilities	Sight, Sound	Sound	Sight	Sight	Sight
Flexibility	Fair	Good Except for Format	Good Except for Format	Poor	Fair
Cost	High Total, Low per Exposure	Low	Low	High Total, Low per Exposure	Low
Availability	Poor	Very Good	Very Good	Fair	Very Good
Ease of Purchase	Easy	Easy	Easy Locally, Difficult Nationally	Easy	Easy

TABLE 1. (Continued)

Media Characteristics	Yellow Pages	Direct Mail	Outdoor	In-Store
Reach	Fair	Poor	Poor	Very Poor
Selectivity	Poor	Very Good	Good Geographically	Very Good
Quality of Reproduction	Poor	Very Good	Very Good	Very Good
Length of Life	Very Long	Moderate	Long	Long
Audience Acceptance	Good	Poor	Poor	Good
Clutter	Poor	Low	Varies	Poor
Multi-Channel Capabilities	Sight	All	Sight	All
Flexibility	Poor	Good	Poor	Good
Cost	Moderate	Total Varies, Low per Exposure	Variable	Low
Availability	Very Good	Very Good	Poor	Very Good
Ease of Purchase	Easy	Easy	Easy	Easy

Independent pharmacies, on the other hand, are restricted to the use of local media, which results in less wasted coverage and is less costly. When located in a small town, the independent pharmacy can make use of all the local media because its trading area corresponds more closely to that of the entire town and there is less excess coverage. But when located in a larger metropolitan area, the independent pharmacy's trading area covers only a portion of the entire city. If coverage were the only consideration, such a pharmacy would advertise exclusively via outdoor media, direct mail, and radio due to their limited reach and greater selectivity. The use of other media would result in the distribution of advertisements to other parts of the city beyond the pharmacy's trading area. The inferior impact of both outdoor and direct mail advertising, however, render them less useful to pharmacy retailers. Instead, independent pharmacies located in both large cities and small towns should use radio and newspaper. The local impact of these media will offset some of the disadvantages due to excess coverage.

REVIEW QUESTIONS (I)

DIRECTIONS: Supply the information requested in each of the following.

1. The size of the audience at which retail advertising is directed is typically

   _____ than the audiences for other advertisements.

2. The type of media and media vehicles a pharmacy retailer is able to use
   and the ways in which they will be used are dictated by his advertising

   _____.

3. The yellow pages and magazines are examples of _____
   media.

4. A medium's coverage is determined by its a)_____

   and b)_____.

5. The amount of time an advertisement is before an audience is called its

   _____.

6. _____ refers to the number of times a message is
   delivered within a specified period.

7. The medium with superior impact due to its use of multi-channel capa-

   bilities is _____.

8. As clutter increases, the impact of an advertisement _____.

9. A medium's flexibility is a function of its timeliness, required ad formats,

   and _____.

10. The amounts of pharmacy resources needed to manage a medium are in-

    fluenced by the medium's cost, availability, flexibility, and _____

    _____.

Check your responses on page 173.

II. MEDIA COSTS

Total advertising costs are composed of production and media costs. While production costs can be significant in magnitude, they are nearly insignificant when compared to media costs. The Bank of America has estimated that media costs account for 90% of advertising expenditures by retailers. As a result, it is not only important to know how media costs are computed, but pharmacy advertisers should also be concerned with the quality of the media time or space purchased.

The ultimate measure of the quality of advertising expenditures is the extent to which advertising objectives have been achieved. However, during the planning stage, when media must be selected, this criterion is not very useful. The most common method of comparing media vehicles is based on the cost per exposure, represented by the following formula:

$$\text{Cost per Exposure} = \frac{\text{Total Ad Costs}}{\text{Total Number of Exposures}/1000}$$

The cost per exposure is simply the total costs of the advertisement divided by the number of people who have been exposed to or have seen the ad. For reasons of convenience, this is normally expressed as the cost per thousand exposures or simply cost per thousand.

A useful variation of this ratio is the cost per effective exposure, in which the denominator is expressed as the number of people in the target market who have been exposed to the advertisement.

$$\text{Cost per Effective Exposure} = \frac{\text{Total Ad Costs}}{\text{Target Exposures}/1000}$$

Other variations are unique to the individual media and will be presented when discussing their costs.

Only television, radio, and newspaper costs will be discussed in the remainder of this unit because these media constitute the majority of pharmacy advertising, and trade practices for these media are relatively standardized. The practices of other media are dependent upon local conditions to a greater extent.

A. TELEVISION COSTS

Television time can be purchased from the network if advertising is to be done on a national basis. While this mode of purchasing TV time may be of interest to large pharmacy chains, most pharmacy advertisers will purchase time from local stations. This is called *spot TV*, and time can be purchased in 10-, 20-, 30-, and 60-second spots. The 10-second spot is called an *ID* and is actually only eight seconds long, with the remainder used for station identification. Twenty-second spots are called *chainbreaks*.

In addition to varying rates by the length of the spot purchased, TV rates vary according to the time of the day and the size of the audience. These factors are incorporated into rate classifications by individual stations, which may be labeled from AAA for the best class to D for the worst. The best time on TV is called *prime time* and occurs from 7 to 11pm, Eastern Standard Time. Fringe time, the hour immediately before and after prime time, is the second best class.

Although TV time is expensive, many stations offer a variety of discounts. Frequency discounts are available when an advertiser agrees to a specific number of spots per week. These are also known as *plan rates*.

Package rates offer a total price for a package of spots at different times of the day. The total price is less than it would be if the spots were purchased individually.

Preemptible rates tend to be lower, because the advertiser gives the station the right to sell his time if it can be sold at a better rate or if it is part of another package. Immediately preemptible rates allow the station to sell the spot at any moment up to the air time. Alternatively, two-week preemptible rates allow spots to be resold only if the original advertiser is given two weeks advance notice. Non-preemptible spots are the most expensive, while immediately preemptible is the lowest rate available.

Rates lower than those published may also be earned by permitting a station to run commercials at its convenience, when the time is available, rather than at specified times. Such a practice is called *run-of-schedule* (ROS) basis.

Lastly, advertisers having large schedules have the opportunity to negotiate with the television station for lower rates.

B.   TELEVISION AUDIENCE MEASUREMENT

Television audiences are measured with rating points. One rating point is equal to 1% of the households, having TV sets tuned to the program of interest. For example, if a pharmacy owner/manager is considering placing advertisements to run during the Saturday ballgame, he should be interested in the games's rating. If he is told the game has a rating of 55, this means that 55% of the households in the market having TV sets will be tuned to the game. The next issue to be resolved is how the market is defined. The closer the definition is to the retailer's definition of his target market, the better.

A gross rating point (GRP) is the program's rating multiplied by the number of times the advertisement runs on the program over a specified period. The convention is to define the period as four weeks. Therefore, if the pharmacy's ad ran on a program with a rating of 10 and it ran twice a week for four weeks, the GRP would be 80.

Rating points and GRP's can be used as the denominators in the cost-per-exposure formula presented earlier. In this way, a pharmacy advertiser can compare the cost per rating point or GRP for ads placed with various programs and select the program that offers the best efficiency. Rating points and GRP's are also used to specify the amount of advertising needed to make an impact. With experience, advertisers are able to determine the number of GRP's that must be achieved before they see the results of their advertising efforts.

C. RADIO COSTS

Radio is similar to television in many respects. First, radio may be purchased for national or local use. However, when used nationally, it is called *spot radio* and when purchased from local stations for local use, it is called, appropriately enough, *local radio*. Another similarity with TV is that the broadcast day is divided into periods in which rates are based on the size of the audience during those periods. The most common periods are:

1. *Drive time.* The most costly period occurs during the time that people are driving to work, from 6 to 10am.

2. *Daytime (or housewife).* This occurs from 10am to 3pm.

3. *Afternoon drive time.* This is the second most costly period and spans from 3 to 7pm.

4. *Evening time.* This period runs from 7pm to midnight.

Sometimes these periods are simply labeled A through D by stations. Time is normally sold in units of 10, 30 or 60 seconds.

The radio discounts available are also similar to those of television. Radio stations offer both preemptible and nonpreemptible time and run-of-station rates. Preemptible run-of-station is the least expensive time offered by radio stations. Also, advertisers can attempt to negotiate for lower rates.

D. RADIO AUDIENCE MEASUREMENT

Radio rating and gross rating points are identical to those for TV in their definitions except that radio rating points are measured as a percent of the population 12 years old or older, in a market, that listen to a particular program. Television rating points are concerned with households. As a result, one radio rating point is 1% of the population 12 years old or older who listen to the radio program on which the advertisement is aired. In performing cost comparisons, pharmacy advertisers can also use radio rating points and GRP's in the denominator of the cost-per-exposure ratio.

E. NEWSPAPER COSTS

Newspaper space is sold by the column line. The width of newspapers is measured in 2-inch columns. Length is measured in agate lines of which there are 14 per inch. So, if a pharmacy advertiser was buying space for a 4-inch by 4-inch (two 2-inch columns) ad and the rate is $1.00 per line, the ad would cost $112.00.

Ad Cost per Column = (4 inches) $\times$ (14 lines/inch) $\times$ ($1.00/line/column)

Like television and radio, newspapers offer a variety of discounts. However, the discounts are usually not offered to national advertisers. The open, one-time, or basic rate is the highest rate against which all discounts are computed.

Quantity discounts are offered on the basis of a total number of lines to be used per period (usually a year). Frequency discounts are always the lowest rates newspapers offer and normally call for a minimum number of ads of minimum size to be placed per week for some period of time. Although the time period is normally a year, 26- and 13-week periods may be used for seasonal merchandising at a higher rate. Under such contracts, no limit is placed on the number of ads or the size of ads that can be placed at the contract rate as long as the minimum is achieved. Often, it is necessary to place "rate holders" which are advertisements used simply to fulfill contracts during slow periods. Institutional advertisements are good for this purpose.

If the pharmacy is faced with widely varying demand, bulk rates may be considered. These contracts base discounts on the total volume of space used during the entire period, thus, allowing the advertiser to concentrate usage during periods of high demand and cut back on the amount of space used when demand wanes.

Short rates are effective when an advertiser defaults by not using the minimum amount of space contracted for in the beginning of a period. The advertiser is required to pay the difference between the rate contracted for and the rate he achieved through usage. For instance, suppose a pharmacy retailer contracted for 1,000 lines at $0.50 per line. But, at the end of the period he only used 750 lines. Every month he was billed at the $0.50-per-line rate but he is actually entitled to the rate for 750 lines, which is $0.60. As a result, his short-rate due is $75.00 (750 × $0.60 less 750 × $0.50).

Conversely, some newspapers will give advertisers a rebate at the end of the year if they have qualified for a greater discount as a result of having used more than the contract specified amount of space. Normally, however, the newspaper will notice that space usage is higher than expected and will suggest terminating the contract and renegotiating a new one.

Newspapers also have rates for run-of-paper (ROP) ads which can be placed wherever the newspaper chooses, although guaranteed positions can be purchased at higher rates. Similarly, color advertisements can be purchased at higher rates. However, color may not be available at all newspapers and when it is, it may be charged a flat rate with large ads costing as much as small ads. Most advertisers who wish to use color ads have them preprinted and inserted into the newspaper.

F. NEWSPAPER AUDIENCE MEASUREMENT

In comparing the cost of newspapers, the rate per line and the newspaper's circulation must be considered. One method for considering both factors is the milline. A milline is the cost per line that would be incurred to reach a circulation of one million with a newspaper using the paper's actual rate and circulation.

$$\text{Milline} = \frac{1,000,000 \times \text{Rate per Line}}{\text{Circulation}}$$

It should be remembered, however, that newspaper space is not sold by the milline. Rather, the milline is simply a convenient index to use in comparing newspapers or different sections of the same newspaper. Sometimes the terms *maxiline* and *miniline* are used. The maxiline is the milline computed at the maximum possible discount, while the miniline is the milline figured at the lowest discount level.

REVIEW QUESTIONS (II)

DIRECTIONS: Supply the information requested in each of the following.

1. Total advertising costs are composed of two components, the largest of which is _____.

2. Total advertising costs divided by the total number of exposures per 1000 people is called the _____.

3. Television advertising rates are varied by the time of day when the ad runs, audience size, and _____.

4. When total advertising costs are divided by the number of people in the target market per 1000 who have seen the ad, the ratio is called the

   _____.

5. Run-of-schedule rates allow a TV station to run commercials at its

   _____ rather than at specified times.

6. The most costly period for advertising on the radio is _____.

7. The lowest rate available from most radio stations is for _____ time.

8. Unlike radio and TV, _____ do not normally offer discounts to national advertisers.

9. The amount an advertiser is required to pay when he fails to use the amount of newspaper space contracted for is called the _____.

10. Newspaper space is sold by the _____.

Check your responses on page 173.

SUMMARY

The selection of a medium in which to advertise is a crucial part of the advertising campaign. The medium used must be capable of reaching the pharmacy's target market, delivering the message, and achieving desired objectives. Furthermore, it must be usable by pharmacy advertisers with limited resources available for the advertising function.

In order to aid pharmacy owner/managers in making optimal media decisions, this unit has discussed the nature of retail advertising, the relationship of advertising objectives to media selection, the various types of media and media vehicles, and cost-related and other characteristics of those media most commonly used by pharmacists.

ANSWERS TO REVIEW QUESTIONS

I.

1. smaller
2. objectives
3. print
4. a.   reach
   b.   selectivity
5. length of life
6. frequency
7. television
8. decreases
9. leadtime
10. ease of purchase

II.

1. media costs
2. cost per exposure
3. length of spot
4. cost per effective exposure
5. convenience
6. drive time
7. preemptible, run-of-station
8. newspapers
9. short rate
10. column line

RECOMMENDED FOLLOW-UP

Those users who would like to learn more about advertising and media selection or would like to enhance their skills in these areas have two immediate opportunities.

First, the references listed below can be studied. These sources, which provided the foundation for this unit, will provide the reader with a wide range of in-depth information on all aspects of advertising. In addition, the topic of advertising is the subject of many other texts and journals.

American Marketing Association, Committee on Definitions. *Marketing Definitions: A Glossary of Marketing Terms.* Chicago: American Marketing Association, 1960.

Anon. *Glossary of Media Terms.* New York: Air Time, Inc., 1970.

Dailey, A. *Advertising Small Business.* Vol. XIII, No. 8 of *Small Business Reporter.* San Francisco: Bank of America, 1976.

Gagnon, J. P. *Managing the Advertising Expense in a Community Pharmacy.* Vol. IV, No. 2 of *The Pharmacist's Business Notebook.* New York: Biomedical Information Corporation, 1980, pp. 3-11.

Haight. W. *Retail Advertising: Management and Techniques.* Morristown, New Jersey: General Learning Press, 1976.

Kleppner, O. *Advertising Procedure.* 6th ed. Englewood Cliffs, New Jersey: Prentice-Hall, Inc., 1976.

The second opportunity pharmacy retailers have is to visit their local media or local advertising agencies to increase their awareness of local facilities and expertise. Both groups have experts in all facets of advertising and will be willing to spend some time with potential advertisers and clients. Such visits have the added advantage of providing the opportunity to gather information about the characteristics of local media discussed in this unit.

POST-TEST

NOTE TO CONTINUING EDUCATION USERS

To obtain CE credit, remove the appropriate sheet from the accompanying answer sheet booklet and follow the directions for completing the post-test and applying for credit.

DIRECTIONS: Circle the letter corresponding to the **one** correct response in each of the following.

1. Retail advertising is different from national or other forms of advertising because

    a. retailers are concerned with buying time or space while other advertisers must also be concerned with other aspects of advertising.

    b. national advertisers normally use the prices of their products in advertisements.

    c. retailers tend to use emotional appeals more than other advertisers.

    d. retailers are concerned with only one level of the channel of distribution, consumers.

2. Advertising objectives that deal with content

    a. specify the people who the advertiser wishes to reach with the advertising.

    b. specify the outcome which the advertiser wishes to accomplish with advertising.

    c. are not concerned with increasing the pharmacy's profits.

    d. are independent of media selection decisions.

3. The signs a pharmacy retailer posts in his pharmacy to promote various products or services are examples of which type of media?

    a. point-of-purchase media
    b. broadcast media
    c. print media
    d. direct advertising media

4. All of the following are examples of advertising media **except**

    a. television and radio.
    b. newspapers and the yellow pages.
    c. *Time* and *Sports Illustrated.*
    d. transit and outdoor advertising.

5. Two variables which influence the impact of an advertisement are

    a. clutter and audience acceptance.
    b. continuity and cost.
    c. reach and selectivity.
    d. availability and ease of purchase.

6. Continuity is defined as

    a. the length of time an advertising schedule runs without interruption.

    b. the number of times the message is delivered within a specified period.

    c. the congruence between the message and the medium used to deliver the message.

    d. the extent to which the audience is influenced by the advertising.

7. Magazines are considered inflexible advertising media because

    a. they do not allow for good geographic or demographic selection.

    b. the availability of space in magazines is not as good as in other media.

    c. they are published infrequently and can reproduce ads in only a limited number of formats.

    d. the leadtime required to place an ad is shorter than in other media.

8. The characteristics of retail advertisements include all of the following **except** the

    a. large involvement of the retailer in all aspects of preparing and running the ads.

    b. large and diverse audience for the ads.

    c. highly factual content of the ads.

    d. almost exclusive use of newspapers.

9. The *Wall Street Journal, Playboy,* and the ABC nightly news are all examples of

    a. local media.
    b. advertising media.
    c. national media.
    d. media vehicles.

10. An advertisement which costs $500 to produce and $2500 in media space, but reaches 10,000 people in the pharmacy's trading area, has a cost per thousand of

    a. $0.30.
    b. $3.00.
    c. $250.00.
    d. $300.00.

11. A television gross rating point is defined as

    a. the percent of households with television sets tuned to a particular program being rated.

    b. the precent of the population over twelve years old with receivers tuned to the program being rated.

    c. the percent of households viewing the program being multiplied by the number of times in a specified time period the program airs.

    d. the total number of households that view a particular program when measurements are taken.

12. One factor to be balanced in the selection of media is the extent to which the audience is influenced by the advertising. This has been labeled

    a. coverage.
    b. impact.
    c. reach.
    d. frequency.

13. The most desirable time to advertise on the radio, when the number of listeners is highest, is

    a. prime time, from 7pm to 11pm.
    b. daytime, from 10am to 3pm.
    c. afternoon drive time, from 3pm to 7pm.
    d. drive time, from 6am to 10am.

14. If a pharmacy retailer knows that the rate for advertising in the local paper is $1.50 per line, and he wants to place a 6-inch by 6-inch ad, the cost will be

    a. $378.00.
    b. $126.00.
    c. $756.00.
    d. $ 54.00.

15. The *Windy City Gazette* has a paid circulation of 1,000,000 people, charges $2.00 per line for advertising, and claims to deliver an average cost per exposure of $0.20. What would be the milline rate if a pharmacist wished to place a 4-inch by 4-inch ad?

    a. $2,000.00
    b. $10.00
    c. $2.00
    d. $0.20

NOTE TO OTHER USERS

The answers to the post-test are provided in the accompanying answer booklet for users who do not wish to obtain continuing education credit.

Unit Eight

Tax Considerations
for the Community Pharmacy

Dewey D. Garner, R.Ph., Ph.D.
School of Pharmacy
University of Mississippi

TABLE OF CONTENTS

Study Time: **1.5 hours**
CE Credit: **.15 CEU**

INTRODUCTION

Legally and economically, tax laws are important to every pharmacy manager. The legal form of a business enterprise is influenced by the federal and state tax laws. Inventory cost (the pharmacy's major investment) and salaries/wages (the pharmacy's major expense) are impacted upon by numerous laws.

This unit is designed for use by practicing pharmacy owner/managers and pharmacy students. Its purpose is to provide basic information on some of the tax considerations essential to independent pharmacy management. A discussion of taxation under the legal forms of business organization including employment, sales, property, and excise taxes, and the impact of depreciation on taxes will be emphasized.

OBJECTIVES

The objectives are presented here to aid the user in focusing attention on expected learning outcomes.

Upon completion of this unit, the user should be able to:

1. Recognize tax advantages and disadvantages of the legal forms of pharmacy ownership.

2. Recognize the legal requirements for election to be taxed as a Subchapter S Corporation.

3. Identify the federal tax benefits of the Subchapter S Corporations.

4. Identify the federal requirements for federal income tax and social security tax programs.

5. Identify the federal requirements for unemployment and workman's compensation laws.

6. Characterize each of the four methods of calculating depreciation as it impacts on taxation.

RECOMMENDED PREPARATION

In order to gain maximum benefit from this unit, it is recommended that the user have some background in tax law. The following references will serve as additional preparation for this unit.

Internal Revenue Code of 1954, Subchapter S—Election of Certain Small Business Corporations as to Taxable Status, Sections 1372-1379.

Election by Small Business Corporation, Internal Revenue Service Form 2553.

Business Taxes, Internal Revenue Service Form 334.

1981 Federal Withholding Tax Tables. Payroll Bulletin No. 4, Volume XXXVII, Englewood Cliffs, NJ: Prentice-Hall, 1980.

Federal Unemployment Tax Act, Sections 7011-7034.

Employer's Annual Federal Unemployment Tax Return, Internal Revenue Service Form 940.

I. TAX CONSIDERATION UNDER LEGAL FORMS OF ORGANIZATION

Whenever a pharmacy is opened, the decision must be made as to which legal form of business will be utilized. The three most common forms are: the sole proprietorship, the partnership, and the corporation. To assess the strengths and weaknesses of each route adequately, a competent accountant is needed to ensure that the pharmacy's tax obligations are met and that the necessary records are available.

A. SOLE PROPRIETORSHIP, PARTNERSHIP, AND CORPORATION

Under a sole proprietorship, business income is taxed as personal income. In a partnership, each person is also taxed on his share of partnership income at the personal income tax rate. Under the corporate form of organization, however, there exists what is known as "double" taxation. The corporation must pay income tax on its earnings, and then the shareholder is taxed again on the part of corporation income personally received. In reality, however, the corporation may elect to distribute funds as salaries to employees, thus lowering corporate profits, so that the actual amounts subject to dual taxation are minimal. Corporate taxation is heavy, but it does have a graduated system which favors smaller corporations. The 1982 rates are:

0 - 25,000	16%
25,000 - 50,000	19%
50,000 - 75,000	30%
75,000 - 100,000	40%
$100,000 and over	46%

B. COMPARISON OF TAXATION UNDER THE PARTNERSHIP AND CORPORATION

Since the taxation methods for the sole proprietorship and partnership are identical, we will compare the partnership with the corporation.

A partner is considered to be self-employed with respect to the social security payroll tax (to be discussed later). As an employee of the corporation, the owner is no longer considered to be self-employed and is not subject to a self-employment rate. His personal withholdings from income must be matched by the employer corporation. Thus, the combined withholding is much greater. The corporation's contribution, however, is a deductible business expense.

Under the Internal Revenue Code (IRC) 105, a partner is not entitled to any tax-free treatment for accident and sickness pay from an employee's accident and health plan. The stockholder employer of a corporation gets limited tax-free treatment for accident and sickness pay.

There is no exception for death benefit payments to partner's beneficiaries. In a corporation, benefits of up to $5,000 are payable tax-free to stockholder employers' beneficiaries.

There are various tax advantages in pension and profit-sharing plans. For example, partners are not proper beneficiaries of an exempt pension trust. The pharmacy cannot deduct payments for partners except under federally qualified plans. Stockholder employers of a corporation can be beneficiaries of a pension trust within the limits established by law.

Corporations may deduct up to 5% of revenue for charitable contributions in addition to the stockholder's 30%. The partnership does not have a deductible amount apart from the individual's 30%.

Partners are not taxed on exempt interest received from the firm. In a corporation, it is taxable income to the stockholder.

Differences exist from state to state between the partnership and corporation with respect to unemployment and workman's compensation. Generally, the differences are not likely to have significant impact.

II. TAX CONSIDERATIONS UNDER THE SUBCHAPTER S CORPORATION

In 1958, the Technical Amendments Act added Subchapter S (IRC S 1371-1379) to the Internal Revenue Code. Subchapter S is an important addition designed to foster the growth of small business. It allows an owner to select the form of business organization desired, without the need to take into account major differences in tax consequence. This addition to the Code allows businesspersons and some professionals the privilege of incorporating and enjoying the advantages of being a corporation without the inherent disadvantage of "double" taxation. A business incorporated under Subchapter S is taxed as if it were a sole proprietorship or a partnership.

A. ELIGIBILITY FOR SUBCHAPTER S INCORPORATION

The purpose of Subchapter S is to foster the growth of small business, and for this reason, not just any business may elect to be taxed as a Subchapter S Corporation. Election is available only to businesses which meet the requirements as prescribed by the law.

1. *Domestic Corporation.* For any business to elect to be taxed as a Subchapter S Corporation, it must be a domestic corporation. This simply means that the corporation must be created or organized in the United States under the laws of the United States or of any U.S. state or territory. This will, probably, not even be a consideration for most pharmacies.

2. *Unaffiliated Corporation.* With only a few exceptions, a corporation may not elect to be taxed under Subchapter S if it is a member of an affiliated group of corporations. An affiliated group is defined by section 1504 of the Internal Revenue Code and essentially means that the corporation may not own 80% or more of both the voting and non-voting stock of any other domestic corporation.

3. *Twenty or Fewer Stockholders.* Any business owned by more than 20 stockholders is not eligible to elect to be taxed as a Subchapter S Corporation. Stock owned jointly by a husband and wife is generally treated as if it were owned by one shareholder. However, if both the husband and wife own stock in the corporation individually, they will be considered as two shareholders.

4. *Individuals or Estates as Shareholders.* No business will qualify as a Subchapter S Corporation if any stockholder is a corporation, trust, or partnership. All shareholders must be individuals or estates.

5. *U.S. Citizens or Residents as Stockholders.* Every stockholder in a Subchapter S Corporation must be either a citizen of the United States or an alien who resides in the United States.

6. *One Class of Stock.* The Internal Revenue Service will disallow the election of any corporation having more than one class of stock. Only the issued and outstanding stock is used to determine the number of classes of stock. Any stock still retained in the treasury of the corporation is excluded. All stock is considered to be of the same class if the stock is identical with respect to the rights and interest which it possesses in the control, profits, and

assets of the corporation. If there is any difference in the voting rights, dividends, or liquidation preference, the IRS will automatically disqualify the corporation from Subchapter S status. In the past, the Internal Revenue Service has ruled that some debts owed the stockholders were, in fact, a second class of stock. The current regulations provide that purported debt obligations which represent equity capital will generally constitute a second class of stock which will invalidate the election. The use of irrevocable voting proxies has been also interpreted as being a second class of stock, for the right of all stockholders to control the corporation is not identical.

The nature of the income produced by a business is not subject to any of the requirements for election to be taxed as a Subchapter S Corporation. However, there are two instances where certain types of income will terminate the election. A Subchapter S Corporation will lose its status, as of the beginning of the taxable year, if 1) more than 80% of the business' gross receipts are derived from sources outside the U.S. or 2) if more than 20% of the business' gross receipts are derived from royalties, rents, dividends, interest, annuities, and sales or exchange of stock or securities.

Even though there is no specific requirement in the law, it has been held that the Subchapter S election is applicable only to a corporation that carries on a trade or business. Under this ruling, it appears that an election will be void from the start if the corporation's activities are not directed toward the realization of a profit.

B. TAX ADVANTAGES OF SUBCHAPTER S CORPORATION

Assuming that the pharmacy will meet the basic requirements for election, the owners must then determine how advantageous such an election would be in light of the various financial aspects of the business.

As a rule, a business may not elect to be taxed as a Subchapter S Corporation if its operation is too large to benefit from the election. The owners of a business generating a large amount of profit may find that it is not advantageous to be a Subchapter S Corporation, because under Subchapter S, all profits are passed through to the owners' personal income and are taxed in the year they are distributed. This large amount of profit would all be taxed at the individual's high personal tax rate, which may be as high as 70%. In this case, the owners may find it better to operate as a regular corporation, paying salaries and issuing dividends in amounts sufficient to cover the owners' needs and leaving the excess profit in the business to be subject to a lower corporate tax rate (16% on the first $25,000). The money left in the corporation will increase the value of the stock or can be paid out as a dividend during years with only a small amount of profit.

The difference between the current corporate tax rate and the individual's tax rate is inversely proportional to the advantage of being taxed as a Subchapter S Corporation. The corporate tax rate is fixed at 16% for the first $25,000. The individual tax rate increases percentage wise (14-70%) as the taxable income increases. Pharmacy owner/managers in very high brackets will find it less advantageous to elect to be taxed under Subchapter S, while those in a more modest range may find it to be of great benefit. A pharmacy owner/manager with a taxable income as high as $50,000 may still find the election profitable.

A pharmacy losing money in the first years of operation is a very likely candidate for Subchapter S treatment. The losses pass through to the owners and are deducted from their personal incomes. However, a business that loses money year after year will exhaust the basis of the stock, and the deduction of any additional losses will not pass through to the owners. A business in this position, or one that is marginal, may find the small additional expense and the legal requirements of a corporation to have more disadvantages than advantages.

A Subchapter S Corporation may be used as a way of splitting income. By utilizing a method of dividing income among a family group and shifting the income from high bracket individuals to persons in low tax brackets, the total family tax burden is reduced. Splitting income may be accomplished by transferring stock to lower-income members of the family such as minor children. This advantage is not available to the sole proprietor or the partner.

Even though a Subchapter S Corporation is treated as a sole proprietor or a partnership for tax purposes, it can still take advantage of many benefits available under the Internal Revenue Code to employees but not to self-employed persons. Though there are some limitations, the pharmacy owner/ manager may participate in advantageous pension and profit-sharing plans. There is also a tax-exempt death benefit of $5,000 which can be paid to a beneficiary; the exclusion of compensation paid during periods of sickness; the payments of premiums for health and accident insurance; exclusion from income of premiums paid by the corporation for group life insurance; and exclusion from income of the value of meals and lodging furnished for the benefit of the employer.

C. SUBCHAPTER S ELECTION

The election to be taxed as a Subchapter S Corporation is a precise process, and if the required procedure is not followed to the letter, the election will be invalid for that entire taxable year. Any eligible corporation may elect to be taxed as a Subchapter S Corporation by filing a statement of election and a statement of consent by the corporation's stockholders. An election that is valid continues indefinitely until it is terminated. There is no need to renew it annually. The decision to elect to be taxed as a Subchapter S Corporation is an important one. One would be ill advised to make such an election without first consulting an attorney and/or accountant.

D. STATEMENT OF ELECTION BY CORPORATION

A corporation desiring to be taxed as a Subchapter S Corporation is required to file Form 2553. This is an extremely simple and straightforward form that requires little more than the name and address of the corporation plus each shareholder's name, address, social security number, and the number of shares owned. The form may be signed by any corporate officer so authorized.

In the case of an existing corporation, the statement of Form 2553 must be filed during the month prior to or following the start of the taxable year. For a new corporation, this statement must be filed within the first month; however, this first month does not begin until the corporation has shareholders, acquires assets, or begins doing business, whichever occurs first. It is important that this form be filed on time. The requirements as to the time for filing an election are explicitly set forth in the statutes and are inflexible. Forms postmarked just one day in excess of the allowed filing period will result in an invalid election.

The statement of election by the corporation (Form 2553) must be filed with the district director for the Internal Revenue District in which the corporation's principal place of business or principal office or agency is located.

Once a Subchapter S election is made by a corporation, it stays in effect as long as the corporation remains in existence, unless it is terminated. As outlined in the statute, there are basically five ways to terminate the election to be taxed as a Subchapter S Corporation. They are as follows:

1. New shareholder failing to consent to the election to be taxed as a Subchapter S Corporation

2. Revocation

3. Ceasing to be a small business corporation

4. Foreign income exceeding 80% of income

5. Passive investment income exceeding 20% of income

The Subchapter S Corporation is a complex and multifaceted legal entity that could prove financially beneficial to many practicing pharmacists. It should be stressed that the decision to be taxed as a Subchapter S Corporation is one that should, generally, not be made without consulting an attorney or an accountant.

REVIEW QUESTIONS (I & II)

DIRECTIONS: Indicate which of the following statements are true (T) and which are false (F) by circling the appropriate letter.

T F 1. Under the partnership business, income is taxed as personal income.

T F 2. As an employee of a corporation, the owner is considered to be self-employed.

T F 3. The employee of a corporation gets limited tax-free treatment for accident and sick pay.

T F 4. There is no exemption for death benefit payments to partner's beneficiaries.

T F 5. Partners are proper beneficiaries of an exempt pension trust.

T F 6. Congress passed the Professional Association Law to allow the professional practitioner to incorporate his practice.

T F 7. Subchapter S is an important addition to the Internal Revenue Service Code designed to foster the growth of small business.

T F 8. A business incorporated under Subchapter S is taxed as if it were a corporation.

T F 9. A Subchapter S Corporation may have no more than 20 stockholders.

T F 10. A Subchapter S Corporation may have two classes of stock.

Check your responses on page 201.

III. EMPLOYMENT TAXES

This section describes requirements for federal income tax, social security tax, unemployment, workman's compensation, and other taxes.

A. FEDERAL INCOME TAX

Federal law requires every pharmacy with one or more employees to withhold federal income tax from wages paid. Every employer must obtain an employer's identification number, required on employment tax returns by filing Form SS-4 with the district director of the Internal Revenue Service. Upon hiring new employees, and at the beginning of each year, the employer should provide every employee with Form W-4, the Employee's Withholding Exemption Certificate.

The amount to be withheld is determined by the number of withholding allowances claimed by employees on this W-4 form. The form should be effective with the first wage payment. When an employee does not give the employer a completed Form W-4, withheld tax should be for a single person with no withholding allowances. A Form W-4 remains valid until a new one is furnished.

The employer must submit to the IRS, at the time and place he files his Form 941, 941-E, or 941-M, copies of Form W-4 he received from employees who claim exemption from income tax withholding if their wages are expected to be more than $200 a week.

Employees may claim all the allowances to which they are entitled for withholding purposes on their Forms W-4. However, they may not claim the same allowances with more than one employer at the same time. A nonresident alien, other than a resident of Canada, Mexico, or Puerto Rico, may claim one special withholding allowance.

In addition to the allowances for personal exemptions, some employees may claim the "special withholding allowance." A single employee with only one employer, or a married employee with only one employer, whose spouse is not working, can claim one special withholding allowance.

Additional withholding allowances can also be claimed on Form W-4 for unusually large itemized deductions, alimony payments, and for allowances based on tax credits (earned income credit, credit for the elderly, credit for child-care expenses, and residential energy credits).

Employees who determine that more tax should be withheld may increase the amount to be withheld by claiming fewer or zero allowances, by asking their employers to withhold more tax, or both. If married, an employee may also check the box titled "married, but withhold at higher single rate," on Form W-4.

Employers may withhold income tax using either: 1) wage-bracket tables or 2) the percentage method. These are the official tables and methods published by the Internal Revenue Service in Circular E, Employer's Tax Guide, Publication 15. For quarterly, semiannual, or annual payroll periods the employer must use the percentage method.

Both the wage-bracket tables and the percentage method give employees the full benefit of allowances claimed.

Wage-bracket tables are set up for weekly, biweekly, semimonthly, monthly, miscellaneous, or daily payroll periods. The table used for a given pay period depends on whether the employee is married or single. The employer must treat an unmarried head-of-household as a single person for this purpose. If the wages exceed the highest wage bracket in the table, in determining the amount to be withheld, the wages may be rounded to the nearest dollar.

Under the percentage method, the tax to be withheld depends on the payroll period, number of allowances, employee claims, and his marital status. To compute the tax, both the allowance and percentage tables published by the IRS in Circular E, Employer's Tax Guide, Publication 15 must be utilized.

To permit more flexibility in an employer's withholding procedures, the Secretary of Treasury can authorize withholding methods which provide substantially the same amount of withholding as do regular methods or withhold the correct amount of tax for the entire year.

Employees who certify to their employers on Form W-4 that they expect to have no federal income tax for the current year, and had none for the prior year, will be exempt from federal income tax withholding. This does not affect the employee's liability for social security taxes.

If at any time, except the third month of a calendar quarter, the amounts withheld from the employees plus the amount of social security taxes owed by the pharmacy equal more than $100, that amount must be deposited in a bank designated as a federal depository. Actual payments to the government are made quarterly, and an annual statement to the Director of Internal Revenue and to the individual employee is required.

B. SOCIAL SECURITY TAX

Federal law requires every pharmacy with one or more employees to withhold social security taxes from wages paid. Social security taxes apply only to a specified amount paid the employee during the year as determined by Congress. The employee's tax rate for 1982 is 6.70%. The taxable wage base for 1982 is $32,400. Sole proprietorships and partners pay a self-employment tax in lieu of social security for themselves. The sole proprietor or partner's tax rate for 1982 is 9.35%. The taxable wage base is $32,400.

The employer is required to match the social security payments made by the employee. The employer is not required to match the social security tax on tips reported by employees. However, employers subject to the minimum-wage provisions of the federal Wage-House Law who pay wages of less than the federal minimum wage (exclusive of tip credit) must pay social security taxes on the difference between the wages paid and the minimum wage.

C. UNEMPLOYMENT

Federal unemployment taxes are paid annually by the employer with no deduction from the employee's wages. The tax applies to every covered employer who, during last or present year, pays wages of $1,500 or more in any calendar quarter, or has one or more employees at any time in each of 20 calendar weeks.

The employer's contribution is a percentage of the employee's wages. For 1982, the tax is 3.4% on the first $6,000 of nonexempt wages paid to an employee during the calendar year, regardless of when wages were earned. The employer's annual Federal Unemployment Tax Return is filed on Form 940 and must be filed by January 31, following the close of the calendar year for which the tax is due. The return should be filed with the IRS service center for the region where the employer's principal place of business is located.

Most states have their own unemployment tax, and it is the responsibility of the employer to register with the appropriate state agency. Contributions to the state unemployment fund are credited against the federal unemployment tax, thus decreasing federal unemployment tax liability. The employer may take credit against federal tax of up to 2.7% for required unemployment taxes paid to a state if the state payments are made on time.

Tax for the first three quarters must be deposited by the last day of the calendar month following each quarter (i.e., April 30, July 31, October 31). No deposit is necessary if tax due for a quarter plus tax due but not deposited for the previous quarter is $100 or less. For the last calendar quarter the employer must compute the balance of tax due for the entire year according to the instructions on year-end return (Form 940). If this balance is more than $100, the entire amount must be deposited by January 31. If the balance is $100 or less, payment may accompany the return.

Every employer subject to tax must keep records of:

1. Total amount of remuneration whether in cash or in medium other than cash (including amounts deducted from such remuneration) paid to employees during calendar year

2. Amount of total remuneration that is wages subject to tax

3. Amount of contributions paid by employer into each state unemployment fund, with respect to service subject to law of such state, showing separately a) payments made and not deducted from remuneration of employees, and b) payments made and deducted from remuneration of employees

4. Information required to be shown on prescribed return and extent to which employer is liable for tax

5. If total remuneration paid (item 1, above) and amount of total remuneration subject to tax (item 2, above) are not equal, reason therefore

6. To the extent material is a determination of tax liability, employer must keep records of the dates in each calendar quarter during which each employee performed services not in course of employer's trade or business, and amount of cash remuneration paid at any time for services performed within a quarter

No particular form is prescribed for keeping the records required. Each employer must use forms and systems of accounting that will enable the district director to determine whether the employer is liable for tax and, if so, the amount.

Every person required, by regulations or by instructions applicable to any form, to keep any copy of any return, schedule, statement, or other document, must keep the copy as part of the records.

Any person claiming refund, credit, or abatement of any tax, penalty, or interest must keep a complete and detailed record as to such tax, penalty, or interest.

All records required to be kept must be kept at one or more convenient and safe locations accessible to Internal Revenue officers. These records must, at all times, be open for inspection by officers of the Internal Revenue Service.

D. WORKMAN'S COMPENSATION

All states have worker's compensation laws. Their purpose is to insure employers against claims for injuries to their employees that are compensable under Compensation Acts, for diseases under Occupational Disease Acts, and/or against liability imposed upon them by law for injuries to employees that are not compensable.

The employer pays the entire cost of workers' compensation, usually by participating in private insurance programs or through a state-operated system. The compensation includes monetary reimbursement and payment of medical expenses. The compensation is based upon a fixed schedule of payments for permanent losses (i.e., a hand or finger), and disability payments are determined by a formula of the employee's earnings.

The workman's compensation and employer's liability policy includes two major sections.

Compensation coverage insures to the full extent of the insured's liability under the Compensation Acts and Occupational Disease Acts of specified states. Claims covered under the applicable act are insured against under this section. The insurance company agrees to pay promptly to any person entitled thereto, under the Workers' Compensation Law, the entire amount of any sum due: "To such person because of the obligation for compensation for any injury imposed upon or accepted by the employer under the applicable statute; and for the benefit of such person, the proper cost of whatever medical or surgical apparatus or appliances and medicine, or, in the event of fatal injury, whatever funeral expenses are required by the provisions of the law."

Employers' liability coverage of the policy is incorporated mainly to provide coverage for employers against suits by, or on behalf of, employees not covered by the Compensation Act or Occupational Disease Act of the state in certain situations, such as the injury of an employee in another state. Only common-law suits based upon personal injuries or disease, as opposed to statutory claims contemplated in the first section, are insured against.

The company will defend, in the name and on behalf of the employer, any suits or other proceedings which may be instituted against him on account of injuries. Such defense includes suits, allegations or demands that are groundless, false, or fraudulent.

Compensation laws are either compulsory or elective. Under an elective law, the employer may accept or reject the act. If he rejects it, he loses the three common-law defenses: assumption of risk, negligence of fellow employees, and contributory negligence. Practically, this means that all the laws, in effect, are "compulsory." A compulsory law requires each employer, within its scope, to accept its provisions and provide for specified benefits.

The Occupational Safety and Health Act of 1970 requires employers to keep three basic records of work-related accidents and illnesses: a log of occupational injuries and illnesses (Form 100), a supplementary record (Form 101), and an annual summary (Form 102). These records must be available at each business location for examination by appropriate officials during regular business hours. They must be kept for five years. Record keeping is not required by federal law for businesses which employ no more than ten full or part-time employees at any one time during the year. State laws may require small employers to keep injury and illness records. Small employers are not exempt from the requirement to report any accident which results in a fatality or the hospitalization of five or more employees.

Additional information concerning the Occupational Safety and Health Act may be obtained by contacting the Acting Regional Administrator, Occupational Safety and Health Administration, U.S. Department of Labor, with appropriate jurisdiction, or you may contact the Office of Information Services, Occupational Safety and Health Administration, U.S. Department of Labor, Washington, DC 20210.

E. OTHER TAXES

Additional taxes which must be considered by the independent pharmacy owner/manager include:

1. *Sales Tax.*   In most states, there exists a state sales tax which must be collected by the pharmacy. Forms must be prepared and reimbursement made at regular intervals, usually monthly, to the state tax commission. Necessities, such as drugs, may or may not be taxed depending upon the state law. Proper records on purchases and sales must be maintained for a specified time period.

2. *Property Tax.*   All pharmacies must pay personal property taxes annually. This tax includes inventory as well as land and building. It is usually collected by a local tax assessor, and a penalty is imposed for delinquent settlements.

3. *Excise Tax.*   Federal excise taxes are imposed on the sale of certain items such as alcohol and tobacco products. These taxes are included in the wholesale price of the products to the pharmacy. It is recommended that the pharmacy owner/manager check with the local IRS office to determine any specialized taxes to which the pharmacy may be subject. The owner/manager should also check with the local tax assessor, since privilege taxes are often imposed on vending machines, food operations, etc.

IV. IMPACT OF DEPRECIATION ON TAXES

Prior to the passage of the Economic Recovery Tax Act of 1981, the Internal Revenue Service recognized four methods for calculating depreciation, the straight-line method and three accelerated methods: 1) declining balance, 2) sum-of-the-year's digits, and 3) remaining-life plan. This section also discusses the accelerated cost recovery system created by the Economic Recovery Act of 1981.

A. STRAIGHT LINE

The simplest method of calculating depreciation is the straight-line method. When used in calculating depreciation, the cost of the asset minus its estimated salvage value is divided by the estimated number of accounting periods in its productive life. The result of this calculation is the estimated amount the asset depreciates each period. For example, if a typewriter costs $600, has an estimated service life of five years, and an estimated salvage value of $100, its depreciation per year by the straight-line method is $100.

B. ACCELERATED METHODS OF DEPRECIATION

The Revenue Act of 1954 liberalized depreciation accounting by permitting depreciation methods for tax purposes which result in higher depreciation charges during the early years of a fixed asset's life. The declining-balance method, the sum-of-the-year's digits method, and the remaining-life plan are all accelerated depreciation schedules permitted under this act.

　　1. *Declining-Balance.* Under the declining-balance method of depreciation, the pharmacy owner/manager is able to write off up to twice the straight-line depreciation rate for the asset without considering the asset's salvage value. Using the previous example an owner/manager could write off 20% each year by the straight-line method. The declining-balance method allows up to 40% (20% X 2) disregarding the $100 salvage value. This would allow a depreciation expense of $240 for the first year ($600 X 40%) as compared to $100 with the straight-line method. In the second year, $144 depreciation (40% X the remaining book value of $360) would be allowed.

　　2. *Sum-of-the-Year's Digits.* Under the sum-of-the-year's digits method, the principle of a progressively smaller ratio is applied to the cost of the asset after subtracting the salvage value. The denominator of the fraction is determined by adding the years in the asset's productive life. The numerator of the fractions are the years of the fixed asset's productive life in reverse order. Using the same example as before, we sum the years (1 + 2 + 3 + 4 + 5 = 15) to get the denominator value of 15. The allowable depreciation for the first year will be $166.67 (5/15 X $500). The depreciation for the second year will be $133.33 (4/15 X $500).

　　3. *Remaining-Life Plan.* The remaining-life plan is a modification of the sum-of-the-year's digits method. The results are exactly the same as the latter. The denominator of the fraction is the sum of the digits of the remaining years of productive life, while the numerator is the number of years of remaining useful life. Using the same example, the allowable depreciation for the first year is $166.67 (5/15 X $500). The depreciation allowance for the second year is $133.33 (4/10 X $333.33).

4. *Summary*. The accelerated methods of depreciation are advocated by many accountants who claim these methods are more equitable in determining the use charge for fixed assets. They point out that, as the asset grows older, repairs and maintenance increase. Therefore, smaller amounts of depreciation allowed in the latter years, when added to the increasing repair costs, give a more equitable total depreciation expense. They also point out that for certain assets the revenue-producing capacity diminishes in its latter years (e.g., building rentals).

The increasing popularity of the accelerated depreciation method is probably more related to tax advantages than to sound accounting theory. Greater write-offs in the early years mean a smaller taxable income and, in effect, also mean the interest-free use for a period of time of the dollars which would have been otherwise paid in taxes under the straight-line method. In the example, the differences were $140, $66.67, and $66.67 respectively, under the three accelerated methods of depreciating the typewriter for the first year. Considering recent inflationary trends, the accelerated methods of recovering a larger portion of the investment as early as possible are very beneficial. In the long run, the choice of method of depreciation depends primarily on the projected total income. If the owner/manager of a new pharmacy is extremely low on capital, he may select an accelerated method to minimize his income tax liability, thus generating additional cash to meet his financial obligations. If the owner/manager has sufficient capital and anticipates a significantly higher net profit in the fourth and fifth years, he would benefit most by the slower but steady depreciation rate of the straight-line method. An owner/manager should also consider the alternative of leasing the asset rather than outright purchase. If a service is leased, this is recorded as a direct expense as it occurs. Thus, the owner/manager is able to write off the entire amount as a business expense in the first year rather than depreciating it over time. Burglary alarm systems and computer services are two areas in which both leasing and purchasing arrangements are common. Tax considerations are one of the most important elements to consider when analyzing the pros and cons of leasing vs. purchasing.

C. ACCELERATED COST RECOVERY SYSTEM

The Economic Recovery Act of 1981 created a new method of depreciation, the Accelerated Cost Recovery System. You must use this new system to calculate depreciation for most assets you placed in service after December 31, 1980. This tax also repealed the election of additional first-year depreciation for assets placed in service after December 31, 1980.

Internal Revenue Service Form 4562 *Depreciation* (revised September 1981) is to be used for tax years ending after December 31, 1980. Part I of Form 4562 is used for most assets placed in service after December 31, 1980. Part II is utilized for assets placed in service before January 1, 1981 and for other assets not qualifying for the Accelerated Cost Recovery System.

Under the Accelerated Cost Recovery System, property falls into one of six classes ranging from three years to fifteen years. The class in which the property is placed depends on whether the property has been assigned a "midpoint class life," under the Asset Depreciation Range System, as of January 1, 1981. These midpoint class lives are listed and explained in Internal Revenue Service Publication 534. Most community pharmacy furnishings are classified as five-year property. Two major exceptions are delivery vehicles (three years) and the building (fifteen years). Three-year property is depreciated at a rate of 25% for the first year, 38% for the second year and 37% for the third year. Five-year property is depreciated 15% for the first year, 22% for the second year and 21% for the third through the fifth years.

Under section 168(b)(3) of the Internal Revenue Service Code, you may elect to use an alternate percentage based on the straight-line method, over a recovery period specified in section 168(b)(3). For three-year property, the recovery periods are three, five, or twelve years. For five-year property, the recovery periods are five, twelve, or twenty-five years.

Let us assume that, in 1981, you placed in service qualifying three-year property with an unadjusted basis of $10,000. Unadjusted basis is the basis used for determining gain less than part of the basis you elected to amortize. Salvage value is not taken into account in figuring your Accelerated Cost Recovery System deduction. You do not elect to use the alternate percentages. For 1981 your deduction will be $2500 ($10,000 × 25%). For 1982 your deduction will be $3800 ($10,000 × 38%) and for 1983 it will be $3700 ($10,000 × 37%).

If you elected the alternate percentages described in section 168(b)(3), your deduction for 1981 and 1984 would be $1670 (½ of 33 1/3 × $10,000). For 1982 and 1983 the deduction would be $3300 ($10,000 × 33 1/3%).

REVIEW QUESTIONS (III & IV)

DIRECTIONS: Indicate which of the following statements are true (T) and which are false (F) by circling the appropriate letter.

T   F   1. Sole proprietors pay a self-employment tax in lieu of social security for themselves.

T   F   2. Every employer must obtain an employer's I.D. number, required on employment tax returns, by filing Form SS-4 with the district director of the IRS.

T   F   3. Federal unemployment taxes are deducted from the employee's wage.

T   F   4. The concept of workman's compensation law is to provide financial assistance to employees for work-related injuries.

T   F   5. The workman's compensation includes both monetary reimbursement and payment of medical expenses.

T   F   6. All states require a state sales tax on prescription drugs.

T   F   7. Inventory is considered property with respect to paying property taxes.

T   F   8. The straight-line method is an accelerated method of depreciation.

T   F   9. Inflationary trends make the accelerated methods of depreciation more preferable.

T   F   10. If a service is leased, it is recorded as a direct expense as it occurs rather than under a method of depreciation.

Check your responses on page 201.

ANSWERS TO REVIEW QUESTIONS

I & II

1. T
2. F
3. T
4. T
5. F
6. T
7. T
8. F
9. T
10. F

III & IV

1. T
2. T
3. F
4. T
5. T
6. F
7. T
8. F
9. T
10. T

RECOMMENDED FOLLOW-UP

It is recommended that the user, upon satisfactorily completing this unit, meet with consultants to discuss the tax issues mentioned in relation to his situation. This approach would be particularly helpful in determining: 1) the appropriate form of legal organization (sole proprietorship, partnership, corporation, or Subchapter S Corporation); 2) the procedures and requirements for withholding federal income tax, social security tax, unemployment, and workman's compensation for employees; and 3) the appropriate schedule for the depreciation of fixed assets.

POST-TEST

NOTE TO CONTINUING EDUCATION USERS

To obtain CE credit, remove the appropriate sheet from the accompanying answer sheet booklet and follow the directions for completing the post-test and applying for credit.

DIRECTIONS: Identify whether each of the following advantages or disadvantages apply to partnership (a), corporation (b), or Subchapter S (c). In each case, write *a, b,* or *c* only on the blank provided.

____1. Benefits up to $5,000 are payable tax-free to a stockholder employer's beneficiaries.

____2. Business income is taxed as personal income.

____3. Exempt interest is taxable interest.

____4. There is a possibility of dividing income among a family group and reducing the tax burden.

____5. Employees are not entitled to any tax-free treatment for accident and sickness pay.

DIRECTIONS: Circle the letter corresponding to the **one** correct answer in each of the following.

6. Which form of legal organization allows the employee to get limited tax-free treatment for accident and sickness pay?

    a. sole proprietorship
    b. partnership
    c. corporation
    d. Subchapter S Corporation

7. Double taxation is a disadvantage of which form of legal organization?

    a. sole proprietorship
    b. partnership
    c. corporation
    d. Subchapter S Corporation

8. Which of the following is **not** an eligibility requirement for election to Subchapter S?

    a. The pharmacy must be a domestic corporation.
    b. The pharmacy must be owned by 20 stockholders or less.
    c. The pharmacy must have more than one class of stock.
    d. No stockholder may be a corporation, trust, or partnership.
    e. Every stockholder must be either a citizen of the U.S. or an alien who resides in the U.S.

9. Which of the following statements is **not** a tax advantage of the Subchapter S Corporation?

    a. It is not subject to "double" taxation.
    b. It may be used as a way of splitting income.
    c. A tax-exempt death benefit of $5,000 can be paid to a beneficiary.
    d. Premiums for health insurance may be paid by the corporation.
    e. It reduces the taxes on income derived outside the U.S. and on excessive gross receipts from royalties, rents, and dividends.

10. Which tax is associated with the W-4 form?

    a. federal income tax
    b. social security tax
    c. unemployment tax
    d. workman's compensation tax
    e. excise tax

11. Which of the following is **not** a requirement for federal income tax?

    a. Income tax must be withheld from wages paid by every pharmacy with one or more employees.

    b. The employer must obtain an identification number by filing Form SS-4.

    c. No employees are exempt from federal income tax withholding.

    d. Payments to the government are made quarterly.

12. Which tax requires the employer to match the funds paid by the employee?

    a. federal income tax
    b. social security tax
    c. unemployment tax
    d. workman's compensation tax
    e. excise tax

13. Which tax is reported on Form 940?

    a. federal income tax
    b. social security tax
    c. federal unemployment tax
    d. workman's compensation tax
    e. excise tax

14. Which of the following is **not** a requirement of federal unemployment taxation?

    a. Taxes are paid annually by the employer.

    b. A percentage of the employee's wages is deducted for unemployment taxation.

    c. The employer is responsible for registering with the appropriate state agency.

    d. Every employer subject to tax must keep records of the amount of total remuneration that is wages subject to tax.

15. The employer pays the entire cost of which tax?

    a. workman's compensation tax
    b. federal income tax
    c. social security tax
    d. excise tax

16. The Occupational Safety and Health Act relates to which form of taxation?

    a. federal income tax
    b. social security tax
    c. unemployment tax
    d. workman's compensation tax

17. The non-accelerated method of computing depreciation is the

    a. straight line.
    b. declining balance.
    c. sum-of-the-year's digits.
    d. remaining-life plan.

18. The method of depreciation which will allow the owner/manager to write off the greatest amount in the asset's first year of useful life is the

    a. straight line.
    b. declining balance.
    c. sum-of-the-year's digits.
    d. remaining-life plan.

19. Which of the following methods of depreciation does **not** consider the asset's salvage value in the computation?

    a. straight line
    b. declining balance
    c. sum-of-the-year's digits
    d. remaining-life plan

NOTE TO OTHER USERS

The answers to the post-test are provided in the accompanying answer booklet for users who do not wish to obtain continuing education credit.